Energy and Entropy in Chemistry

Energy and Entropy in Chemistry

P. A. H. Wyatt

The University of Sheffield

Macmillan
London · Melbourne · Toronto
St. Martin's Press
New York

MACMILLAN AND COMPANY LIMITED
Little Essex Street London WC2
also Bombay Calcutta Madras Melbourne

THE MACMILLAN COMPANY OF CANADA LIMITED
70 Bond Street Toronto 2

ST. MARTIN'S PRESS INC.
175 Fifth Avenue New York NY 10010

First published 1967

Demy 8vo, 208 pages
18 line illustrations

Library of Congress Catalog Card Number 67–24401

Printed in Great Britain by Richard Clay (The Chaucer Press), Ltd.,
Bungay, Suffolk

Contents

Preface

In this book I have tried to shorten the path to chemical thermo-dynamics for beginners by building upon ideas acquired at school in elementary physics and chemistry. Most of the topics normally included in an undergraduate course are nevertheless touched upon, though the detailed suggestions for further reading should be followed up when amplification is needed: in this way some familiarity with authoritative books in the field will soon be acquired. Moreover, to provoke an early practical acquaintance with Latimer's *Oxidation Potentials* and the Pitzer and Brewer revision of Lewis and Randall's *Thermodynamics*, some of the problems have been specifically designed to depend upon having these books at hand.

Chemical potentials figure prominently from the beginning and the connexion between free energy and chemical equilibrium is reached as quickly as possible. It is hoped that some of the lines of argument introduced to cope with the consequent rearrangement of material will ease the transition to a later course in statistical mechanics without impeding progress along the more abstract path to phenomenology.

Although the relevance of the reaction isotherm is fairly obvious, the chemical thread is probably harder to follow through parts of chapters 6 and 7. Beginners should therefore avoid some of this detail at a first reading and try to pick out familiar landmarks in chapter 8, where such well-known phenomena as osmotic pressure, the depression of freezing-point and the variation of vapour pressure with temperature are all put into perspective. Those initially baffled by physical arguments expressed mathematically may there be reassured by finding that the appropriate formulae are all derived by the same method, which simply requires a knowledge of the way chemical potentials vary with temperature, pressure and composition, just as stated on p. 10 in the first chapter. Given this key, all the derivations can be studied and practised together.

Finally, the book expresses a point of view which, it is hoped, will prove interesting to the more experienced chemist as well as helpful to the beginner. Thanks are due to students and colleagues for encouraging comments when these chapters were issued as lecture notes and particularly to Dr. J. A. Leisten for persuading me to write a book at all.

P. A. H. Wyatt

Sheffield, July 1966

Principal Symbols Used

Despite a preference for E, the internationally accepted U is adopted for energy. On the other hand, I reluctantly denote the Helmholtz function by A rather than F for the present because the problems lean so heavily upon books in which F stands for the Gibbs function that confusion might arise. Two of Everett's suggestions are taken up: lower case italics for (partial) molar quantities and the superscript $\ominus$ for a standard state in general. (*An Introduction to the Study of Chemical Thermodynamics*, Longmans, 1959; see also the translation of *Chemical Thermodynamics*, Prigogine and Defay, Longmans, 1954.)

To avoid clumsy suffixes, the activity of a substance M is sometimes conveniently denoted by (M) and its molality by $[M]$; and heat and work are denoted by small Roman letters in general and by large ones when the changes take place reversibly.

The chemical species to which a quantity refers is indicated by a subscript and the phase where necessary by a superscript; e.g. $^{\alpha}h_i$ is the partial molar enthalpy of species i in phase α (where α may be replaced by the specific symbols s, l, g for solid, liquid and gas). The common post-superscripts are $\ominus$, already mentioned, and $°$ for a standard state which to be a pure substance (including a gas at 1 atm pressure).

A	Helmholtz free energy	ν	number of moles in stiochiometry
a	activity		
C	heat capacity	ω	degeneracy of a molecular state
c	partial molar heat capacity	P	total pressure
$\textsc{c}$	number of components	p	partial pressure
Δ	increment of a property	$\mathscr{P}$	number of quantum states for a given energy
E	electromotive force		
e	half-cell electrode potential	$\textsc{p}$	number of coexistent phases
ϵ	energy of a molecular state	π	osmotic pressure
F	the faraday, 96,493·5 coulomb per mole of electrons	Q	heat absorbed reversibly
		q	heat absorbed in general
f	rational activity coefficient, 'true' ionic activity coefficient	R	gas constant, 1·987 cal deg^{-1} mole^{-1} or 8·315 $\times$ 10^7 erg deg^{-1} mole^{-1}
$\textsc{f}$	number of degrees of freedom		
G	Gibbs free energy	S	entropy
γ	molal activity coefficient	s	partial molar entropy
H	enthalpy	T	absolute temperature
h	partial molar enthalpy	θ	proportionality constant (Chapter 4), freezing-point depression (Chapter 8)
I	ionic strength		
K	equilibrium constant in general		
K_p	equilibrium constant in terms of partial pressures	U	total energy
		u	partial molar energy
k	Boltzmann's constant	V	volume
k_f	cryoscopic constant	v	partial molar volume
l	molar latent heat (enthalpy of phase change)	W	maximum work done by system
		W'	maximum work available
m	molality	w	work done by system in general
μ	chemical potential	x	mole fraction in condensed phase
N	number of molecules	y	mole fraction in vapour phase
n	number of moles	z	'valency' of an ion

1

The Measurement of the Tendency to Change

§ 1.1 **Work and potential energy**

From elementary physics we learn that work can be done by taking advantage of the tendency of bodies to pass from regions of high to regions of low potential: falling water can be harnessed to turn wheels and the difference of electric potential at the live and neutral mains sockets can be used to drive motors. But remember that in the development of the simple theory it is the notion of *work* that comes first, while the *potential energy* of a body in some specified state (10 cm distant from a large mass, for example) is defined in terms of the work required to bring the body to this state from a chosen zero (such as an infinite distance away). After this only consistency is required: the work done against forces in changing the potential between definite limits becomes available in exactly the same amount when the change is allowed to proceed in the opposite direction between the same limits. Of course, full advantage is not always taken of the work available and changes of potential can, and frequently do, occur without any work being done at all. The book-keeping is then kept straight by the introduction of heat into the balance, but this complication will be considered later.

According to the definition of potential energy then, changes which are brought about against the forces in operation are accompanied by an increase in potential energy, while those allowed to occur in the natural direction are accompanied by a decrease in potential energy. A quantitative measure of the tendency to change spontaneously from one condition to another is therefore given by the potential difference involved, and when no conceivable small change in condition can produce a decrease in potential there is no tendency to change and the body is at equilibrium. (Small changes are specified to cover the case that a stone in a hollow on the side of a hill is at equilibrium, although a large displacement may send it rolling down into the valley. This is important, since many interesting chemical molecules are in the position of the stone in the hollow, being fundamentally unstable with respect to dissociation into their elements.) Potential energy can thus be used as a criterion of equilibrium.

§ 1.2 The work rule and reversibility

The same idea can be expressed more simply in terms of the work from which the notion of potential energy was derived: *A spontaneous change can in principle be harnessed to yield work. The maximum work available (W') is a measure of the tendency of the change to occur.* This will be referred to as the work rule.

It is sometimes difficult to think of a way to harness certain processes (though special imaginary devices such as selective membranes have been invented to make the idea more acceptable), but this is not a serious drawback to applying the rule, as our primary interest is usually in the tendency of the change to occur or in the formulation of an equilibrium condition, not in the production of work in a practical way.

The basic idea is this: A spontaneous process left to itself brings about changes in a definite direction. Imagine an apparatus set up in such a way as to oppose this tendency to-

2

wards change by the application of forces of some kind. If the forces are slightly overestimated the process will be forced to go in the opposite direction; while if the forces are exactly balanced no change will occur at all. On then reducing the applied forces infinitesimally, advantage can be taken of the maximum capability of the system to do work, as the following mechanical example may help to make clear.

Think of a truck on rails at the top of an incline. By means of ropes and pulleys the tendency of the truck to move can be harnessed to lift heavy weights from one floor of a building to another, for example (or to turn the armature of a dynamo). The movement of the truck can naturally be made to do different amounts of work by lifting different weights: the lighter the weight, the faster the truck will move down the incline — the greater its kinetic energy. There is, however, an upper limit to the amount of work it can do, and this can be measured in terms of the weight that just balances it. A very slight reduction in this weight will allow the truck to move very slowly down the incline (with very little kinetic energy), doing an amount of work very near to the maximum work. By slightly increasing the weight the truck can be pulled slowly back up the incline. For this reason, when the tendency to change is harnessed to the maximum extent the system is said to be operating *reversibly*.

§ 1.3 Potential energy and work in chemistry

The extension of these ideas to chemistry is not as difficult as it seems at first sight. Just as with physical changes, spontaneous chemical processes can in principle be opposed and even reversed by the application of suitable forces. When the chemical change is only just allowed to proceed in the natural direction the (maximum) work done against the applied forces measures the tendency of the change to take place. Quantities called *chemical potentials*, represented by the symbol μ, have just the properties required for putting this idea on a numerical basis. For simplicity, only isothermal (constant-temperature) processes will be considered at this stage.

Each substance i in a mixture, or in the pure state, has a chemical potential μ_i. Thus μ_{H_2O} and $\mu_{C_2H_5OH}$ stand for the chemical potentials of water and ethanol in a given aqueous solution of alcohol. But the values of these potentials vary with the composition of the mixture (and with the temperature and pressure): $\mu_{C_2H_5OH}$ is greater in a solution containing 60% of alcohol than in one containing 40%, and the increase is measured by the amount of work done in transferring a gram-molecule (a *mole*) of alcohol from a large quantity of the 40% to a large quantity of the 60% solution. The 'large quantity' is specified to make the compositions to which the μ_i refer quite definite. If a mole of ethanol (46 g) were taken from 1 kg of the 40% and added to 1 kg of the 60% solution, clearly the overall compositions of the '40' and '60'% solutions, and hence the μ_i values, would alter significantly during the process. This effect would be smaller for 10 kg quantities and smaller still for 100 kg; and the larger the weights of solution taken, the more nearly the measured quantity of work approaches the true value of μ_i (60%) $-$ μ_i (40%). To the question 'how large a quantity?' therefore, the practical answer is: large enough so that the small changes in μ_i caused by the removal and addition of the substance are within the experimental error of the work measurement (or can be allowed for in some way by suitable corrections). Of course it is not necessary to transfer a mole in an actual experiment; a much smaller quantity can be transferred and the result multiplied up to the amount per mole.

In general terms, *the difference $\mu^B - \mu^A$ in the chemical potential of a given substance in the two states A and B is measured by the work that has to be done by an external agent to transfer a mole of the substance reversibly from the state A to the state B* (it being understood that the amounts of material in states A and B are large enough for μ^A and μ^B to remain constant throughout). Very often it is

4

convenient to regard the chemical potential of a substance (element or compound) as having already been determined in some specified state and to proceed from there. Such a state is called a *standard state*, and the corresponding chemical potential will be represented in general as $\mu^{\ominus}$. The standard state is often taken as the pure substance at 1 atm pressure and for this common special case the simpler symbol μ° will be used; but when a different convention is adopted for the solute in dilute solutions the general symbol $\mu^{\ominus}$ will be retained for clarity. The value of μ° depends upon the temperature and is also generally different for the solid, liquid and gaseous forms of the same substance.

A very important step now, from the chemical point of view, is to recognize that μ° for a compound is not independent of the μ° values of the elements that form it. The reason is that 'dissociated into its elements' can be thought of in a sense as one of the states of the compound. For example, one of the possible states of the material of composition NH_3 is a mixture of nitrogen and hydrogen gases in the ratio of 1 mole to 3. Half a mole of N_2 and one and a half moles of H_2 can be withdrawn from such a state, converted by a reversible process to one mole of ammonia and then added to a vessel containing ammonia in some specified condition. The overall work done by an external agent when all the processes concerned are reversible is then a measure of $\mu^{\circ}_{NH_3} - \frac{1}{2}\mu^{\circ}_{N_2} - \frac{3}{2}\mu^{\circ}_{H_2}$ if all the species are in their standard states. The advantage of this is that it reveals a common scale for the potentials of all compounds. Thus, any other compound of nitrogen and hydrogen, such as hydrazine, N_2H_4, has its potential referred to the same scale as ammonia, and hence the work of conversion of it to ammonia can be calculated once the potentials of both are known relative to the elements. All the potentials are thus sure to be consistent: the potential of ammonia, say, in a specified state must be the same whether it is arrived at from the work of formation directly from the elements or from hydrazine plus hydrogen.

Otherwise it would be possible to dissociate ammonia (reversibly) into its elements and then reform it (reversibly) via hydrazine and obtain work from the whole process; but according to the work rule this would imply a net tendency for ammonia to change to ammonia, which is nonsense.

Quantities like $\mu°_{NH_3} - \frac{1}{2}\mu°_{N_2} - \frac{3}{2}\mu°_{H_2}$, which measure chemical potentials relative to the elements at the same temperature, are known as '*standard free energies of formation*', for reasons which will soon emerge. For convenience, the reference forms of the elements are chosen to be those in which they commonly occur at 25 °C and 1 atm pressure; e.g. hydrogen as a gas composed of H_2 molecules, mercury as a liquid, carbon as graphite and phosphorus as white phosphorus (the common though not the most stable form).

Experiments always yield *differences* of chemical potentials between two states and, provided that all μ values are referred to the common scale through the elements, the ultimate choice of the scale zero is arbitrary. It is nevertheless helpful to think of μ as the work of transferring a mole from a state of zero potential to the state of interest: the *chemical potential energy* of the system is then increased by $\mu_i dn_i$ when the small amount dn_i mole of the substance i is added to it, as happens with electrostatic potential energy when a charge de is added. Since in any application the dn_i mole has to be transferred from some other state on the same scale, the arbitrary constant in μ_i is always removed in practice when the difference is taken.

§ 1.4 The importance of μ

If μ for a substance is not the same in all parts it can reach in a system work can evidently be made available by harnessing its transference down the potential gradient from regions of high to regions of low μ, and this can go on until μ is the same throughout the accessible regions. In simple terms, a high μ is associated with a high concentration, or pressure, and a low

μ with a low concentration. Hence μ is the quantity which determines the tendency of a substance to diffuse from one region to another, or to pass, say, from the solid to the liquid phase, for these two phases cannot be in equilibrium until μ has the same value in both. For example, if μ is higher in a piece of ice than in the surrounding water, H_2O molecules will tend to pass from the solid to the liquid, i.e. the ice will tend to melt. But everybody knows that this process can be stopped by lowering the temperature, which means that the sensitivity of μ to temperature in ice and water must differ in such a way that cooling permits the equalization of μ in the two phases.

But μ has a deeper chemical significance still: chemical potentials not only give the direction of physical processes like diffusion and phase transformations, they also determine the tendency of substances to transform themselves into one another by chemical reactions. The basic reason for this is that in any chemical equation, e.g.

$$C_6H_6 + HNO_3 = C_6H_5NO_2 + H_2O$$

both sides contain the elements in exactly the same amounts, and so the work of forming the reactants is automatically referred to exactly the same zero as the work of forming the products from the elements. The difference in the work of formation of the substances on the two sides of the equation then measures the work available from the reaction in either the forward or the reverse direction, and so tells which way the change can proceed spontaneously.

Consider now a system composed of a number of substances which interact chemically. Take n_i to be the number of moles of the substance i present, and μ_i to be its chemical potential. If small changes are made in composition the system gains in chemical potential energy by $\mu_i dn_i$ for each small increase dn_i in the number of moles of each substance (μ_i being the change *per mole*), and the total change in potential energy of the system is given by the sum of such terms, written $\sum_i \mu_i dn_i$. (The changes have to be small in general, since the μ_i may alter as the additions are made, thus necessitating integrations for the calculation of the work, as happens when the electrical potential alters on charging a parallel-plate condenser.) Now, from this point of view, a chemical reaction is nothing more than a special case of the addition and removal of substances in which the dn_i are always proportional to the stoichiometrical numbers, ν, in a chemical equation such as

$$\nu_A A + \nu_B B + \ldots = \nu_C C + \nu_D D + \ldots \qquad (1.1)$$

This represents a reaction between ν_A moles of A, ν_B moles of B, etc., giving as products ν_C moles of C, ν_D moles of D, etc.

During such a reaction the potential energy of the system increases by $(\mu_C dn_C + \mu_D dn_D + \ldots)$, i.e. the sum of the $\mu_i dn_i$ terms for the products, and decreases by $(\mu_A dn_A + \mu_B dn_B + \ldots)$, the similar sum for the reactants. But the overall decrease in potential energy gives the work available from the small chemical change:

$$(\mu_A dn_A + \mu_A dn_B + \ldots)$$
$$- (\mu_C dn_C + \mu_D dn_D + \ldots) = dW' \qquad (1.2)$$

or, since the dn_i are in the same ratio as the ν_i,

$$(\nu_A \mu_A + \nu_A \mu_B + \ldots) - (\nu_C \mu_C + \nu_D \mu_D + \ldots) = W' \qquad (1.3)$$

W' in this equation must now be understood to mean the maximum work available from the amount of change represented by the numbers of moles, ν_i, in equation (1.1) when the potentials μ_i are fixed at the values they happen to have in the system: this merely puts the amount of work on a convenient chemical scale. When appreciable changes take place, the μ values do, of course, increase or decrease continuously as concentrations build up or diminish in the system.

We now have a criterion for the direction of chemical change. If the left side of (1.3) is positive the reaction (1.1) can proceed to the right; if it is negative the reaction can only proceed spontaneously to the left; if it is zero the system must be at equilibrium. The left-hand side of equation (1.3) is usually known as the decrease of *free energy* of the reaction: thus *the free energy decreases in a spontaneous reaction and does not change at all if the system is at equilibrium.*

To return to the ammonia example,

$$N_2 + 3H_2 = 2NH_3$$

the quantity which really determines whether ammonia will increase at the expense of nitrogen and hydrogen is therefore

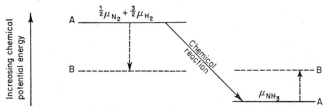

FIG. 1.1   At A nitrogen, hydrogen and ammonia gases are mixed in a vessel and are not initially at equilibrium. By chemical reaction the pressures (and hence the chemical potentials) of nitrogen and hydrogen are decreased while the pressure (and μ) of ammonia is increased until the state B is reached when $\frac{1}{2}\mu_{N_2} + \frac{3}{2}\mu_{H_2} = \mu_{NH_3}$

the free energy change $2\mu_{NH_3} - (\mu_{N_2} + 3\mu_{H_2})$: if this is negative the change can proceed in the forward direction (ammonia formation); if it is positive the change can only occur spontaneously in the backward direction; and if it is zero the system is at equilibrium. See Fig. 1.1. It is significant that the numbers which occur as the coefficients of μ in expressions of this kind are exactly the same as those which occur before the corresponding substances in the chemical equation.

What must be done to investigate equilibrium problems in chemistry is now clear. If the case is one of the distribution of a substance between phases the conditions have to be changed in such a way as to make μ the same in the phases concerned.

9

If a chemical reaction is being considered adjustments have to be made so that the $\nu_i\mu_i$ sum is the same for reactants and products. In either case *what is required is a set of quantitative rules for the variation of chemical potentials with changes in the most common experimental conditions, namely temperature, pressure and concentration.*

§ 1.5 Gibbs and Helmholtz free energies

Fixing the temperature with a thermostat does not fix all the conditions for an experiment. A reaction vessel may be completely enclosed, in which case the volume is held constant, or it may remain throughout at the constant pressure of the atmosphere so that volume changes can occur. The potential sums, $\sum_i \nu_i\mu_i$, still control the direction of change and the position of equilibrium in both cases, but the actual values of the sums at the end of the experiment will be different in the two cases if the reaction at constant pressure is accompanied by any change in the volume, since clearly the final conditions of the products will then be recognizably different. The amount of work available on harnessing a spontaneous reaction therefore generally depends upon the experimental conditions adopted, and for convenience two free energy functions are defined to cover the two cases. One of these is much more useful than the other, as most reactions are carried out at constant pressure.

The work available for harnessing when a reaction is carried out at constant volume is given by the decrease in the *Helmholtz free energy*, A; at constant pressure it is given by the decrease in the *Gibbs free energy*, G.

These conditions are put into symbols in the following way. The maximum work obtainable from the change is represented as before by W' and the change in any quantity like G is always written using the symbol Δ: ΔG stands for the value of G at the end of the change minus the value of G at the beginning.

Suffixes provide a convenient way of indicating which variables are held constant: thus $W'_{T, P}$ stands for the maximum work available when a change is carried out at constant temperature and pressure. In these terms therefore

$$\Delta G = -W'_{T, P} \qquad (1.4)$$

$$\Delta A = -W'_{T, V} \qquad (1.5)$$

the minus signs showing that when a positive amount of work is available the free energy change must be negative. (1.4) is much more commonly employed than (1.5), and when the expression 'free energy' is used in chemistry without qualification it is almost always the Gibbs function G that is meant.

§ 1.6 Available and unavailable work

The work rule and the subsequent discussion have been carefully worded in terms of the work 'available for harnessing' by an external agent. The reason is that the total work may include work done against the balanced forces specified in the experimental conditions, and work of this kind is completely earmarked for expenditure in this way and unavailable for harnessing externally. Only the residue, the available work, then determines the tendency to change, since this tendency can only be opposed by altering the variables still accessible to alteration.

Pressure is force per unit area. Thus, when boundaries move to accommodate a change of volume at constant pressure this force moves its point of application and work is done. If a reaction involves an increase of volume at constant pressure, therefore, part of its inherent capacity for undergoing change is used up in doing work against the atmospheric pressure; and this capacity becomes exhausted, and equilibrium is established, sooner than would be the case for the same reaction carried out at constant volume. On the other hand, if a volume *decrease* accompanies the reaction the atmospheric pressure will actually push the reaction farther on.

In the case of the most important balanced force therefore, all this is summarized by saying that the available work, W', is equal to the total work less the work done by the system against the pressure of the atmosphere. Since this latter work is given by $P\Delta V$ (§ 2.1),

$$W' = W - P\Delta V \qquad (1.6)$$

If ΔV is negative, $W' > W$; if ΔV is zero W' and W are the same. (Hence (1.5) could also have been written in the form $\Delta A = -W_{T, v}$, but the W' form was used to emphasize that this is always the fundamental quantity determining the direction of change: it just happens to be equal to W in this case.)

§ 1.7 Direct free-energy measurements

There are two ways of looking at equation (1.4). On the one hand, G represents the net result of all the various factors affecting the chemical potentials of all the substances in the system; so a detailed assessment of all the various contributions for products and reactants will provide an estimate of W' from which conclusions about the existence of equilibrium or the direction of change can be drawn. On the other hand, the equation also means that, whatever the factors that go into the make-up of G, *changes* in this quantity can be evaluated experimentally through W' when this is accessible to measurement: a chemical reaction has somehow to be carried out reversibly at constant temperature and pressure.

Both aspects are important, but evidently the second requires no further preparation and can be followed up immediately.

Equation (1.4) is not nearly so remote from ordinary experience as it might appear. In general, factors such as friction often impede the realization of reversible conditions experimentally, but there is an important practical device which approaches reversibility closely enough to permit accurate measurements to be made of the tendencies of many chemical reactions to occur. This is the *potentiometer*.

The experimental arrangement is indicated in simplified form in Figure 1.2. The cell under investigation is connected in

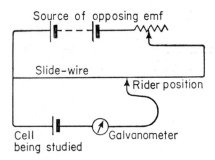

FIG. 1.2

series with a centre-zero galvanometer, which shows how much current is flowing through the cell and in which direction it is flowing. It is also connected in series with a variable length of the potentiometer slide-wire, along the whole length of which a fixed, calibrated potential drop is maintained by means of a source of opposing electromotive force (e.m.f.) such as an accumulator.

This apparatus clearly has the elements of a reversible device: a position of balance (no current in the galvanometer) can be found, and the current can be made to flow in either direction through the cell by slight movements of the rider on the slide-wire away from this balance point. What is important to chemistry is that the flow of current through the cell coincides with the occurrence of a chemical reaction in the natural or the unnatural direction, according to the direction of current flow. No current at all means that the tendency of the chemical reaction to take place is exactly balanced by the opposing e.m.f. and can thus be measured very precisely.

For example, a rod of zinc dipped into a solution of cupric sulphate becomes coated with a layer of copper, because of the tendency of a chemical reaction to take place:

$$Zn\ (s) + Cu^{2+}\ (aq) = Zn^{2+}\ (aq) + Cu\ (s) \quad (1.7)$$

(The descriptions in brackets, (s) for solid and (aq) for aqueous solution, are often included in the chemical equations in quantitative work.) By separating the reactants in a Daniell cell, the spontaneous change can be made to yield work. Schematically the cell is represented thus:

$$Zn \mid ZnSO_4\ (m_1) \mid CuSO_4\ (m_2) \mid Cu \quad (1.8)$$

which means that an electrode of zinc dips into a zinc sulphate solution which is in liquid contact (through a porous pot usually) with a cupric sulphate solution, into which dips an electrode of copper. The two solutions are of specified composition (m_1 and m_2), since this affects the free energy of reaction (1.7) and hence the e.m.f. of the cell.

At each electrode there is a constant interchange of ions between the metal and the solution, but the more electropositive metal, zinc (with the greater tendency to pass into solution as positive ions), develops a greater excess of electrons and so becomes the negative pole of the cell when it is connected to an external circuit. When the cell does work externally the electrons flow away from the zinc electrode, which then loses more ions to the solution and acquires more free electrons to keep up the flow; while at the copper electrode ions pass from the solution to the metal in numbers equivalent to the electrons arriving there through the connecting wires.

Notice at this stage that if you are unsure which is the spontaneous direction of the cell reaction you have only to observe experimentally which is the positive electrode: this is where the electron-consuming reaction occurs — the addition of electrons to Cu^{2+} to form Cu in the present case. By convention the positive electrode is written on the right in schemes like (1.8) (when the appropriate cell reaction, e.g. (1.7), corresponds to the natural direction of the chemical change).

At the balance point on the potentiometer the applied e.m.f., E, is just sufficient to stop the cell reaction occurring. A slight shift of the rider permits the cell to do work against an e.m.f. slightly smaller than E, say $E - \delta$, and this means that for every coulomb passed through the cell $E - \delta$ joules of work will be done. The δ can be made as small as you like, so the maximum work per coulomb is E joules. Conventionally chemical equations like (1.7) are taken to refer to gram molecular quantities. Thus the amount of charge carried through the cell during the chemical change (1·7) would be two faradays (2 F), i.e. 2 × 96,493·5 coulombs, because two moles of electrons are involved. Hence, in this case the maximum work available from the extent of reaction represented by the chemical equation is 2FE. In general, for a reaction involving n moles of electrons,

$$W' = nFE = -\Delta G \qquad (1.9)$$

Notice that W' and ΔG depend on the quantity of reaction considered, whereas E does not: E is an *intensive* quantity, ΔG an *extensive* one. (Quantities, like total volume, which depend on the size of the sample considered in the given state are extensive; those, like composition and density, which do not are intensive.)

Not all electrochemical reactions which can be formulated like (1.7) are capable of functioning reversibly; and it must also be admitted that the junction between the two liquids produces a complication in accurate work, though by no means all cells have these liquid junctions. Nevertheless, many chemical reactions can in fact be harnessed to form cells reversible enough for their free energies to be measured in this very direct way.

Problems for Chapter I

1. Which of the following properties are extensive and which are intensive? Volume, density, pressure, refractive index, thermal capacity, specific heat, free energy, chemical potential.

2. Write down the chemical reactions which occur when 1 faraday is passed in the spontaneous direction through the following cells:

(a) Zn (s) | Zn(NO$_3$)$_2$ (m_1) ‖ TlNO$_3$ (m_2) | Tl (s)
$$E = 0.427 \text{ volt}$$

(b) Tl (s) | TlNO$_3$ (m_2) ‖ Pb(NO$_3$)$_2$ (m_3) | Pb (s)
$$E = 0.210 \text{ volt}$$

(The central double line means that the liquid junction potential can be taken to have been eliminated.)

Calculate in each case the ΔG for the reaction you have written. From these results calculate ΔG for the reaction

$$\text{Zn (s)} + \text{Pb}^{2+} \text{(aq, } m_3) = \text{Zn}^{2+} \text{(aq, } m_1) + \text{Pb (s)}$$

3. G and A are precisely related by the equation $G = A + PV$, where P is the pressure and V the total volume of the system; and G (not A) is always equal to $\sum_i \mu_i n_i$. Accepting the constant temperature relation

$$\sum_i n_i \mathrm{d}\mu_i = V \mathrm{d}P$$

which will be understood later, show that $\sum_i \mu_i \mathrm{d}n_i$ is given by $\mathrm{d}G$ for isothermal changes at constant pressure and by $\mathrm{d}A$ for isothermal changes at constant volume.

(*Hint*: Consider the result of the general differentiation of G,

$$\mathrm{d}G = \mathrm{d}A + P\mathrm{d}V + V\mathrm{d}P = \sum_i \mu_i \mathrm{d}n_i + \sum_i n_i \mathrm{d}\mu_i \quad (1.10)$$

The reason that $\sum_i \mu_i n_i$ is more simply related to G than to A

is that you can integrate $\sum_i \mu_i dn_i$ very easily keeping T and P constant and changing all the dn_i in such a way as to keep them always in proportion to the n_i originally present. This keeps all the μ_i constant (because of the fixed temperature, pressure and composition) and so

$$\Delta G = \int dG = \int (\mu_1 dn_1 + \mu_2 dn_2 + \ldots) = \sum_i \mu_i \Delta n_i \quad (1.11)$$

The same cannot be done with ΔA, since the μ_i are bound to change as you force more material into the system at constant volume: hence the appearance of PV terms.)

2

An Important Consequence of the Way the Chemical Potential of a Gas Depends upon its Partial Pressure

Most chemists feel uneasy about the introduction of 'work' into chemical arguments, for the very understandable reason that since a tendency to change can obviously manifest itself quite freely without any work being done at all, the ability to perform work cannot be its most fundamental feature. It may help, therefore, to regard 'work' as having to do with the recognition and *measurement* of a tendency to change and not with its *explanation*, which will be taken up in molecular terms in Chapters 4 and 5. Similar misgivings may be felt about the mechanical contrivance introduced below to make the idea of measuring chemical potentials more tangible, but a detailed grasp of illustrations of this kind is not essential for the understanding of the remainder of this book, especially as equations like (2.9) can be derived in other ways later. The object of this chapter is to arrive at *and use* the very important equations (2.9) and (2.14) without introducing any new ideas.

§ 2.1 The work of expansion

The total force exerted by a pressure P (force per unit area) over an area A is PA. If the boundary of a vessel moves through a distance d against this force, the total work done by the substance in the vessel is PAd, i.e. the pressure multiplied by the volume swept out, or $P\Delta V$. If ΔV is negative the work done by the substance is negative, which means to say that work is done upon the substance.

The $P\Delta V$ formula is directly applicable as it stands to cases like expansion against the atmospheric pressure, in which the whole change in volume takes place against a constant pressure. If, however, the pressure changes during the expansion from V_1 to V_2 the work has to be calculated from the integral

$$\text{w} = \int_{V_1}^{V_2} P \mathrm{d}V \qquad (2.1)$$

which can be evaluated if P can be expressed in terms of V. A small w is used here for work, since the capital is reserved for maximum work. (2.1) gives the work of expansion correctly, whether maximum or not, provided that P stands for the external pressure against which the expansion occurs. If P is only infinitesimally smaller than the actual pressure of the system itself, w and W are the same: if the system expands into a vacuum, $P = 0$ and no external work is done at all.

§ 2.2 How the chemical potential depends upon the pressure when the temperature is fixed

Consider the work required to transfer reversibly one mole of a fluid from a very large reservoir where its pressure and molar volume are P and v to a very large reservoir where its pressure and molar volume are $P + \mathrm{d}P$ and $v - \mathrm{d}v$. (The convention of using a capital letter for the total value of an extensive property like volume and a small letter for the corresponding quantity per mole will be adopted throughout: thus $v_i = V/n_i$ for a pure substance.) In any actual experiment the removal or addition of a mole of a substance would, of course, affect the pressure in the reservoir slightly, but this effect can be made as small as desired by increasing the size of the reservoir. Alternatively, only a small fraction of a mole need be transferred and the changes can be multiplied up to the amounts per mole.

In Figure 2.1 the large vessels, to the left and right of the junction A, are brought together so that the transfer can be controlled in a simple way. At A there is a valve which can be opened to allow access of material from the left to the movable piston (of negligible mass) just to the right. This piston also has a valve which can be opened when required; and it is made of iron so that it can be moved evenly by a magnet around the tube. The movement of this magnet is controlled by an external agent and is the means of doing work on the system.

The transfer of 1 mole from the left to the right vessel is carried out in three stages:

1. With the piston valve closed, open the valve at A and pass the magnet along the tube from A to B, a distance corresponding to the molar volume v. The external agent only has to supply a force equivalent to the constant pressure difference dP exerted over the area of the piston, and the volume ΔV traced out under this constant pressure is the molar volume v. Hence, *work done by external agent* = $v dP$.

2. Close the valve at A and allow the piston to adjust very slightly so that the pressures are equalized on each side of it to $P + dP$ and the molar volumes to $v - dv$. The distance traced out by the magnet corresponds to the volume change $-dv$ and the work done (*on* the external agent) must be less than $dv dP$, since the pressure difference does not stay at dP throughout the slight change. But $dv dP$ is a second-order differential and can be made absolutely negligible by making

the infinitesimals as small as you like. For a differential change therefore, *the work contributed at this stage is zero.*

3. No further work is done when the piston is returned with its valve open to its former position at A, thereby completing the transfer.

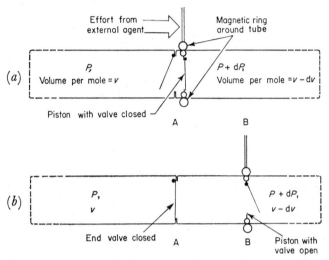

FIG. 2.1   Measuring the change of chemical potential with pressure (§ 2.2) (*a*) transfer of one mole begins. (*b*) after transfer of one mole

Thus, the work done by an external agent in transferring one mole of the substance from the state at pressure P to that at pressure $P + dP$ is vdP, and this is therefore a measure of the differential increase in the chemical potential of the substance:

$$d\mu = vdP \qquad (2.2)$$

whence *the variation of μ with pressure at constant temperature is measured by the molar volume.* Working from the standard state at 1 atm $(P°)$, when μ is $\mu°$, μ is therefore calculable at another pressure P by the formula

$$\mu = \mu° + \int_{P°}^{P} vdP \qquad (2.3)$$

This equation actually applies to solid, liquid or gas, but the effects of pressure are much larger for gases, since v is much greater than for condensed phases.

§ 2.3 The chemical potential of a perfect gas

A perfect gas obeys the simple gas laws and its pressure, volume and temperature are related by the equation

$$PV = nRT \qquad (2.4)$$

where n is the number of moles of gas in the sample. For one mole of gas,

$$Pv = RT \qquad (2.5)$$

T, the temperature on the gas scale, is defined by this equation and has a zero at $-273 \cdot 15°C$, and the gas constant R is assigned a value such that the degree on the gas scale is the same as the degree Centigrade. The magnitude of R ($= Pv/T$) depends upon the units in which P and v are measured: its value in cc atmospheres per degree per mole (cm³ atm deg⁻¹ mole⁻¹), for example, can be calculated from the expression $1 \times 22{,}414 \cdot 6/273 \cdot 15$, since 1 mole of a perfect gas occupies $22 \cdot 4146$ litres at 1 atm pressure and 0°C. To convert to c.g.s. units you have to remember that 1 atm is equivalent to $1 \cdot 01325 \times 10^6$ dyn cm⁻² (from $980 \cdot 665 \times 76 \times$ density of mercury). The value of R in cal deg⁻¹ mole⁻¹ is $1 \cdot 987$.

The perfect gas is of such importance because it has properties to which those of real gases tend at low pressures. Except when high pressures or intermolecular forces are specifically investigated, it is generally quite sufficient for ordinary work to use equation (2.4) for all gases.

At a fixed temperature, T, for the change of one mole from a pressure $P°$ to a pressure P, equation (2.5) requires that

$$\int_{P°}^{P} v \, dP = RT \int_{P°}^{P} \frac{dP}{P} = RT \ln \left(P/P° \right) \qquad (2.6)$$

Therefore, from (2.3)

$$\mu = \mu^\circ + RT \ln (P/P^\circ) \qquad (2.7)$$

Since the standard state for a gas is 1 atm, this equation can be simplified when P is expressed in atmospheres:

$$\mu = \mu^\circ + RT \ln P \qquad (2.8)$$

(Notice that substitution of P in mm Hg in (2.8) would be equivalent to adopting a new standard state of 1 mm Hg: to preserve the 1 atm standard state with P in this unit (2.7) is used with $P^\circ = 760$ mm Hg.)

In the case of a perfect gas, the product Pv is independent of P and v at a fixed temperature, so that $Pdv + vdP$ is zero; and hence the same result is obtained by integrating either vdP or $-Pdv$. This is a very special result, however, and is ultimately due to the absence of attractive forces between the molecules of a perfect gas, whence there is no intermolecular potential energy to be altered as the molecules are pushed closer together on increasing the pressure.

§ 2.4 Chemical potentials in a mixture of perfect gases

Dalton's law of partial pressure applies to a perfect gas mixture: the partial pressure exerted by a component gas in a mixture is the same as the pressure it would exert if it occupied the same volume without the other components present. It then follows that the work done in transferring a mole of a perfect gas of partial pressure p_i to a state in which its partial pressure is $p_i + dp_i$ is $v_i dp_i$, whether other gases are present or not.

To see this, imagine a device differing slightly from Figure 2.1 in that the valve in the piston, when opened, permits only the molecules of the substance of interest to pass through and is impermeable to all others, while the valve at A, when closed, has just the opposite effect and is permeable to all substances other than the one of interest. The cycle of operations is similar to that used above, with the piston now tracing out the volume v_i, but a new feature is that, while the substance i only differs in partial pressure by dp_i in the two reservoirs, there may in general be an appreciable total pressure difference ΔP because of the arbitrary pressures of the other gases. The external agent therefore does work to the extent of $v_i \Delta P$ in stage 1, but recovers v_i ($\Delta P - dp_i$) of this in stage 3, when the piston is returned, with its special valve open, to position A. (Stage 2, in which p_i equalizes, here involves $\Delta P dv_i$ which also cancels in Stage 3.) The net work done by the external agent in the process is therefore $v_i dp_i$, and this is the increase in the chemical potential of i in the mixture.

By use of the formula $p_i v_i = RT$ as before,

$$\mu_i = \mu^\circ_i + RT \ln p_i \qquad (2.9)$$

§ 2.5 Chemical equilibrium in a gaseous system

Equation (2.9) is all that is required to make a very important extension to the argument of § 1.4. For the ammonia synthesis, for example, equation (1.3) gives

$$2\mu_{NH_3} - \mu_{N_2} - 3\mu_{H_2} = -W' \qquad (2.10)$$

But by substitution of (2.9) and slight rearrangement,

$$(2\mu^\circ_{NH_3} - \mu^\circ_{N_2} - 3\mu^\circ_{H_2})$$
$$+ RT \ln (p^2_{NH_3}/p_{N_2}p^3_{H_2}) = -W' \qquad (2.11)$$

(Notice how the stoichiometric numbers appear as powers when they are taken inside the logarithmic term.)

When the system is at equilibrium two simplifications can be made: $W' = 0$ and $p^2_{NH_3}/p_{N_2}p^3_{H_2} = K_p$, the ordinary mass-action equilibrium constant.

Hence $\qquad (2\mu^\circ_{NH_3} - \mu^\circ_{N_2} - 3\mu^\circ_{H_2}) = -RT \ln K_p \qquad (2.12)$

The general formula for a gas equilibrium easily follows from equation (1.3) in the same way:

$$(\nu_C\mu_C^\circ + \nu_D\mu_D^\circ + \ldots - \nu_A\mu_A^\circ - \nu_B\mu_B^\circ - \ldots) = -RT \ln K_p \tag{2.13}$$

where $K_p = p_C^{\nu_C} \times p_D^{\nu_D} \ldots / p_A^{\nu_A} \times p_B^{\nu_B} \ldots$, the suffix p here indicating not constant total pressure but that the equilibrium constant is expressed in pressures.

Equation (2.13) is often expressed in terms of ΔG°, *the standard free energy change of the reaction* thus:

$$\Delta G^\circ = -RT \ln K_p \tag{2.14}$$

ΔG° stands for the increase in the free energy associated with the conversion of reactants to products (in quantities specified by the chemical equation) when they are all in their standard states, and its value is determined by the choice of standard states (pure gases at 1 atm here), as is the value of K_p by the corresponding choice of units. If each of the μ°_i in (2.13) is replaced by the corresponding standard free energy of formation (by subtracting the μ° values of the elements), the value of the left-hand side is quite unchanged, since the μ° terms for the elements must cancel out. ΔG° for a reaction can therefore be obtained from the sum of the standard free energies of formation of the products less the sum for the reactants.

(It would have been unnecessarily restrictive, however, to have used $\Delta G = 0$ in the simplification of (2.11), since this is the equilibrium condition appropriate to constant overall pressure and so would imply a restriction on the variations of the equilibrium partial pressures such that they always added up to a fixed value. All that is really required is that the μ_i should be given by (2.9) and be independent of the presence or absence of other gases, whatever the total pressure may be. Since ΔG° is a fixed quantity at a given temperature, it then follows that the pressure quotient K_p is also fixed whatever the partial pressures may add up to, just as most chemists would expect.)

At high pressures, when deviations from (2.4) become serious, equation (2.14) can still be saved by expressing K_p in terms of *fugacities*, or effective pressures, which replace the p_i in (2.9); but this fortunately is unnecessary at ordinary pressures, except for work of the highest precision.

Equation (2.14) is known as *the reaction isotherm* and may also be encountered in the form $K_p = \exp(-\Delta G^\circ/RT)$.

§ 2.6 Standard free energies and the calculation of equilibrium constants

G. N. Lewis set out to tabulate the standard free energies of formation of all known substances, and his results up to 1923 were collected in the first edition of *Thermodynamics*, by Lewis and Randall. Given a complete table of this kind, the equilibrium constants of all conceivable gas reactions are calculable through ΔG° and (2.14). For example, since the standard free energies of formation of the elements are zero, K_p for the ammonia synthesis reaction follows simply from a knowledge of the standard free energy of formation of ammonia, viz. $-16,350$ joule mole^{-1} or $-32,700$ joule for 2 moles at 25°C. Thus

$$K_p = \exp(+32,700/8 \cdot 315 \times 298 \cdot 15) = 5 \cdot 4 \times 10^5 \text{ atm}^{-2}$$

The units are atm^{-2} because two more pressure powers appear in the denominator of K_p than in the numerator in this case, and the number $8 \cdot 315$ is the appropriate value of R (in joule deg^{-1} mole^{-1}) when ΔG° is expressed in joule mole^{-1}.

Such a large equilibrium constant shows that the percentage of ammonia at equilibrium is very high at 25°C, but it is well known that the reaction is too slow to be economical at this temperature even in the presence of a catalyst, and industrially a much higher temperature is used to speed it up. (The yield has then to be increased by using high pressures.)

This story is not complete, of course, until the variation of chemical potentials with temperature has been considered; but once this has been done $\Delta G°$, and hence K_p, can in principle be found for any temperature of interest. A more urgent question at present is how the standard free energies which appear in Lewis and Randall's tables were obtained. The answer is that they were first calculated from equilibrium constants by the exact reverse of the argument just employed for the calculation of K_p for the ammonia synthesis. Beginning with compounds with standard free energies obtainable directly from elementary synthesis, more complex reactions involving these compounds could then be employed to give the free energies of other compounds for which direct synthesis is experimentally impracticable. Thus the whole table could be built up by a step-wise process. What is required at each stage is the equilibrium constant of a reaction for which only one of the free energy terms in $\Delta G°$ is unknown.

Chemical equilibria do not form the only source of free energy data, however: calorimetry and spectroscopy have played an increasingly important role since 1923, and it is now often convenient to tabulate the wealth of data in terms of other functions which will be explained later.

§ 2.7 Chemical equilibrium in solution

To extend (2.14) to reactions in solution, all that is necessary is to set up an expression analogous to (2.9). This is done by defining a quantity called the *activity*, a, according to the equation

$$\mu_i = \mu^\ominus_i + RT \ln a_i \qquad (2.15)$$

The whole derivation is then followed through as before, but with a_i in place of p_i everywhere, so that the equilibrium constant becomes

$$K = a_C{}^{\nu_C} \times a_D{}^{\nu_D} \ldots / a_A{}^{\nu_A} \times a_B{}^{\nu_B} \ldots \qquad (2.16)$$

The standard free energy of the reaction, $\Delta G^{\ominus}$ is still of the form given by the left-hand side of equation (2.13), but for dilute solution equilibria the standard chemical potentials, $\mu^{\ominus}$, usually refer to special unit concentration conditions rather than to the pure components, except for the solvent itself. The general form of (2.14) in terms of any chosen set of standard states is therefore

$$\Delta G^{\ominus} = -RT \ln K, \qquad (2.17)$$

where the choice of standard states determines the units of K. (2.14) is a special case of (2.17).

The dependence of the activity upon the concentration is the central problem of the quantitative treatment of solutions, but without further detail at this stage some idea of the significance of the extension of the reaction isotherm to solutions can be obtained.

At equilibrium μ_i for a volatile substance in solution must be the same in the vapour as in the solution phase. The standard potentials, $\mu^{\ominus}{}_i$, will, however, differ in the two phases (unless the vapour pressure of i happens to be 1 atm at the solution standard state), so that (2.9) and (2.15) require that the logarithms of p_i and a_i differ by a constant amount: i.e. p_i must be proportional to a_i. Now it happens that in dilute solutions p_i tends to be proportional to the concentration of i, whence it follows that in dilute solutions the activity can be approximately equated to the concentration; and when concentrations are substituted for activities the equilibrium constant (2.16) takes on the form familiar in elementary work. Thus the standard free energy for the hydrolysis of ethyl acetate can be obtained approximately from $[C_2H_5OH][CH_3COOH]/[CH_3COOC_2H_5]$, the concentration expression. Notice that the omission of the solvent concentration [H_2O] from this formula (because it hardly changes) is really equivalent to setting its activity at unity throughout and defining the standard state of water as the pure liquid, since $a_{H_2O} = 1$ demands $\mu_{H_2O} = \mu°_{H_2O}$, by (2.15). This $\mu°_{H_2O}$ has to be remembered when the standard free energy of the reaction is broken down into its components:

$$\Delta G^{\ominus} = \mu^{\ominus}_{C_2H_5OH} + \mu^{\ominus}_{CH_3COOH} - \mu^{\ominus}_{CH_3COOC_2H_5} - \mu°_{H_2O}$$

(Think of the balanced chemical equation when writing down the $\mu^{\ominus}$ terms for $\Delta G^{\ominus}$.)

Sometimes, especially when dealing with non-electrolytes in dilute solutions, concentration is a good approximation to activity; but this is not the general rule, and quite serious errors can be introduced in this way for some equilibria involving electrolytes. Much is known about the relationship of activity to concentration in such cases, however, and useful (though slightly complicated) approximations are still available for systems in which the activities have not been experimentally determined.

Notice particularly that a_i in (2.15) can be multiplied by any constant, b, without affecting the value of the physically significant μ_i, provided that $\mu^{\ominus}_i$ is adjusted by a constant amount $(-RT \ln b)$, which is equivalent to shifting the standard state to $\mu^{\ominus}_i - RT \ln b$. The scale of activity is therefore arbitrary and can be adjusted for convenience when necessary by altering the standard state: the numbers obtained at various concentrations for the activity of a given substance referred to one standard state are simply proportional to those referred to another. For example, although for most aqueous equilibria the standard state of water itself is taken as the pure solvent, when comparisons between different solvents are required water has sometimes to be treated in the same way as the solutes and assigned the activity $1,000/18 = 55.5$ instead of unity in the corresponding formula for the equilibrium constant. This is equivalent to shifting the standard state of water away from the pure solvent.

Problems for Chapter 2

1. The standard free energies of formation at 25°C of the gases N_2O, NO and NO_2 are 24·9, 20·72, 12·39 kcal mole^{-1}. Are these three oxides stable or unstable with respect to dissociation into their elements?

Write down chemical equations for the formation of NO_2 (g) (1 mole) from each of the other two oxides and oxygen and calculate the corresponding equilibrium constants. (1 cal = 4·184 joule, T at 25°C = 298·1°K, 2·303 log$_{10} x$ = ln x.)

Discuss briefly (but quantitatively) the extent of conversion of NO to NO_2 at atmospheric pressure in the presence of oxygen.

2. $\Delta G°_{298}$ for the formation of atomic hydrogen is 48·57 kcal mole^{-1}. (The 'mole' of atomic hydrogen is, of course, the gram-atom.) Calculate the equilibrium fraction of hydrogen dissociated into atoms at 1 atm pressure and 25°C.

3. A quantity of dinitrogen tetroxide was completely vaporized in a large flask at 0°C. The pressure was found to be 25·8 mm Hg, but the vapour density was only three-quarters of that calculated for this pressure from the formula N_2O_4. Calculate the equilibrium constant and $\Delta G°_{273}$ for the reaction

$$N_2O_4 \text{ (g)} = 2NO_2 \text{ (g)}$$

(In thinking of the density, remember that the volume occupied by a gas at a fixed temperature and pressure is proportional to the number of molecules it contains. Formulate the partial pressures of N_2O_4 and NO_2 in terms of α, the fraction of N_2O_4 molecules dissociated, before attempting to write down an expression for K_p. Be careful about muddling mm Hg with cm Hg too.)

4. Why cannot vapour densities be used for investigating the extent of dissociation of hydrogen iodide into hydrogen and iodine in the gaseous phase?

5. How do the standard free energies and equilibrium constants of the following reactions differ?

(a) N_2 (g) + $3H_2$ (g) = $2NH_3$ (g)
(b) $\frac{1}{2}N_2$ (g) + $\frac{3}{2}H_2$ (g) = NH_3 (g)

3

Heat, Work and Energy

To understand fully the factors which contribute to the chemical potentials and to their variation with temperature, it is necessary to consider the relationship between heat, work and energy. In itself the study of energy changes also leads to important information about the strength of chemical bonds.

§ 3.1 Heat and work

When two bodies at different temperatures are put into contact, heat passes from the hotter to the colder until the temperatures are equalized. In molecular terms, the molecules in the hotter body have a higher average kinetic energy (per degree of freedom) than those in the colder, and energy is transferred until the average kinetic energy is equalized. The quantity of heat required to raise the temperature of a body by $1\,°C$ is the *thermal capacity* of the body (represented by the symbol C): the thermal capacity per gram is the *specific heat* and the thermal capacity per mole the *molar heat capacity* (represented by c). The heat unit, the *calorie*, used to be defined as the specific heat of water between $14.5°$ and $15.5\,°C$.

The same effect of increasing the temperature of a body can be produced by doing work on it. For example, a force applied to a moving paddle in a liquid moves its point of application and work is done. If the paddle rotates in the liquid a definite amount of work is done at each rotation, but the rotational motion does not persist for long when the paddle stops. In molecular terms rotational motion is very unlikely, requiring all the molecules in an element of volume to have, superimposed upon their normal random motions, a common velocity component in one direction relative to their surroundings. The disturbances at the walls of the vessel and at the paddle disorganize this motion and average out the extra kinetic energy over all possible directions, among all the molecules: that is, the temperature rises by a definite amount for a definite amount of work done. This equivalence of the effects of work and heat was demonstrated experimentally by Joule, who showed that whatever contrivance was used for performing measured amounts of work, there was always a strict proportionality between the work done and the amount of heat required to produce the same effect.

Work is measured in *ergs* (dyn cm), or multiples of this unit such as the *joule* (10^7 erg) or the *kilojoule* (10^{10} erg); and since amounts of work are definable with greater precision than amounts of heat, the *calorie* is now defined in terms of work units as 4·184 joule. (This is very near to the 15° calorie defined in terms of the specific heat of water.) In chemistry it is often of interest to measure the heat evolved or absorbed on mixing certain substances together, and when this is done an electrical heater is incorporated into the calorimeter so that the temperature change may be directly compared with that produced by a definite amount of electrical energy (calculable from the product of the current, potential difference, and time). Because of this dependence of heat measurements on work units, it has been recommended that the calorie should be suppressed as a unit and all thermal quantities expressed in joules. This rational suggestion has not been adopted with any enthusiasm, however, and most chemical quantities will be found expressed in cal and kcal, even when, like ΔG, they are measurable in terms of work.

§ 3.2 Total energy

A system of fixed composition exchanges energy with its surroundings only by means of heat (including radiation) or work. Any change in its total energy can therefore be defined in terms of the heat absorbed, q, and the work done (*by* the system), w, as

$$\Delta U = q - w \qquad (3.1)$$

U is used for the total energy and ΔU for the final value less the initial value, just as with the functions G, A and V. Both q and w can be either positive or negative: negative q means that heat is evolved and negative w (producing a positive U increment) that work is done *on* the system. Equation (3.1) sums up the equivalence of the effects of work and heat, for U, like G, A and V, depends only on the state of the system and not on how this state is arrived at. A change can be brought about by adding a certain amount of heat or doing an equivalent amount of work on the system, or by a combination of the two. Thus q and w can vary widely in transitions between two fixed states, but their difference must always be the same. When the change is carried out reversibly and the fixed maximum amount of work (W) is done, the amount of heat absorbed in the process must also be fixed and may be represented by the symbol Q. This is clearly an important quantity, as it holds the key to the relationship between W (and W′) and ΔU. Only changes in U are defined by (3.1), and this is all that is really required for chemistry: a convenient reference point for the total energy scale is, however, provided by the absolute zero of temperature.

§ 3.3 How the total energy varies with temperature

By holding the volume constant, so that no mechanical work is done, and arranging that no other kind of work is done at all, the whole of a small increment in U, dU, can be measured by the heat added. If the thermal capacity of the system at constant volume is represented by C_v and the increment of temperature by dT the heat added is $C_v dT$.

Thus
$$dU = C_v dT \qquad (3.2)$$

or
$$(\partial U/\partial T)_{V,\,n_i} = C_v \qquad (3.3)$$

The curly ∂ symbols are used instead of ordinary d's to emphasize that this is a partial differential coefficient: it behaves just like an ordinary differential coefficient when the other variables to which U is sensitive are held constant throughout any change. C_v is itself temperature dependent: it has to be expressed as a function of T and the right-hand side integrated to give the change in U over any large range of temperature.

Notice that dU between the same states is given by (3.2) whether the change is brought about solely by the addition of heat or not, since both U and C_v depend only on the state of the system.

§ 3.4 The heat of a chemical process at constant volume

Imagine a closed and rigid vessel filled with water or an aqueous solution of sodium hydroxide and having a sealed glass bulb containing sulphuric acid immersed in it. The vessel is completely stoppered, perfectly insulated and then shaken so that the glass bulb breaks. Whether the vessel contains water only or a solution of sodium hydroxide, the temperature rises. In the first case we speak of a heat of dilution and in the second a heat of reaction, but both are examples of chemical processes of types commonly investigated by calorimetry. An exact calibration with an electrical heater of the heat required to produce the observed temperature rise then gives a direct measure of the U change accompanying the chemical process in each case.

This is not obvious from the specification of the experiment, which both demands that no external work is done (constant volume) and that no heat enters or leaves the system (insulation), whence w = 0, q = 0 and therefore ΔU = 0. But we know from (3.2) that an increment ΔT on its own would indicate an increase in U of $C_v \Delta T$, so it must follow that the chemical process is accompanied by a *decrease* in U of just this amount, since the overall change in U is zero. Another way of saying the same thing is that $C_v \Delta T$ is the amount of heat the system would have given up to its surroundings to keep its temperature constant had the process been carried out in a thermostat. As a matter of fact, isothermal calorimeters are sometimes used, and in these the quantity of heat required to maintain isothermal conditions is actually measured instead of a temperature rise, but adiabatic (insulated) calorimeters are much more common.

With this understanding of q as the heat absorbed at constant volume when a chemical process is carried out under isothermal conditions (although measurable in an adiabatic experiment), we write

$$(\Delta U)_{V, T} = q \qquad (3.4)$$

Since the change in U for a chemical process is sensitive to temperature (depending upon a difference of C_v terms), the temperature increment is kept small by using small amounts of reacting substances in an actual experiment, and the result is then multiplied up to molar quantities to give the ΔU appropriate to the quantities specified in a definite chemical equation.

The bomb calorimeter, used extensively for the determination of heats of combustion of organic compounds, yields ΔU values.

Calorimetry is not, however, the only source of information

on energy changes in chemistry. Precisely measured energy amounts can be absorbed by a molecule as radiation and the limit of a series of electronic jumps (detectable in *molecular spectroscopy*) gives the energy required to break a bond and detach an atom or radical from the parent molecule. Or again, the energy for bond-breaking can be acquired from an electrical potential gradient: hence the use of 'appearance potentials' for radicals in *mass spectrometry*.

§ 3.5 Enthalpy and changes at constant pressure

If the mixing experiment described above (§ 3.4) is carried out in a vessel open to the atmosphere the conditions differ in that an amount of work $P\Delta V$ is necessarily done against the atmosphere when there is a change of volume. When no other work is done, therefore, the change in total energy is $(q - P\Delta V)$. Thus

$$(\Delta U)_{P,\,T} + (P\Delta V)_{P,\,T} = (\Delta[U + PV])_{P,\,T}$$
$$= (\Delta H)_{P,\,T} = q \quad (3.5)$$

The terms $U + PV$, which give the required change $\Delta U + P\Delta V$ at constant pressure, are grouped together to define the new function H, which plays the same role at constant pressure as U does at constant volume. For the q of (3.5) is to be understood as the heat absorbed at constant pressure when a chemical process is carried out isothermally, although like the q of (3.4) it is usually obtained from adiabatic experiments. Notice too that in adiabatic calorimetry at constant pressure it is H, not U, that remains constant, since q = o but w = $P\Delta V$.

The function H, defined as $U + PV$, is known as the *enthalpy*. Since U, P and V have fixed values determined only by the state of the system, the same must apply to their combination H, which therefore becomes a further function of the state of the system with useful properties. Not only is it directly related to the heats of reactions carried out at constant pressure; it also determines the temperature dependence of the equilibrium constants of these reactions. Notice that dH is only equal to $dU + PdV$ when the pressure is constant. In general, $dH = dU + PdV + VdP$.

§ 3.6 The temperature dependence of the enthalpy

The corresponding equation to (3.3) is easily derived from the thermal capacity at constant pressure, C_p, since the heat absorbed in raising the temperature by dT is given both by $C_p dT$ and by dH.

Thus
$$(\partial H/\partial T)_{P,\, n_i} = C_p \qquad (3.6)$$

It has been found that the variation of c_p with temperature for many substances can be represented empirically by an equation of the form

$$c_p = a + bT + cT^{-2} \qquad (3.7)$$

in the range of T between 298° and 2,000° on the gas scale, in which T must be expressed: this corresponds to about 25° to 1,700°C. With this equation, (3.6) can be integrated to give H at any temperature in the range relative to its value at one such temperature; the constant a is, of course, purely empirical and does not represent the value of c_p at $T = 0$, since the equation (3.7) fails at low temperatures. (A slightly simpler form

$$c_p = a' + b'T + c'T^2 \qquad (3.8)$$

is often encountered, but (3.7) has been found to represent data with greater precision.)

An advantage of using a common form like (3.7) for all substances is that usually in chemistry differences of sums of c_p values are required for the following reason. Just as for the free energy, the overall change in H, ΔH, for a reaction of type (1.1) is given by the difference between the sums of terms for products

38

and reactants, except that in this case the sums are of the type $\sum_i \nu_i h_i$ instead of $\sum_i \nu_i \mu_i$. Just as before, the molar enthalpies, h_i, are related to the same reference states for reactants and products, viz. the elements in their standard conditions, so that

$$\sum_i (\nu_i h_i)_{\text{products}} - \sum_i (\nu_i h_i)_{\text{reactants}} = \Delta H \qquad (3.9)$$

does give correctly the overall change in H accompanying the chemical reaction. But differentiation of this equation with respect to T will, by (3.6), simply give a series of terms $\nu_i c_{pi}$ in place of the $\nu_i h_i$ with just the same signs as these on the left-hand side, and $(\partial \Delta H / \partial T)$ on the right. The equation can be tidied up by using the same convention with regard to the Δ for C_p as for H:

$$(\partial \Delta H / \partial T) = \Delta C_p \qquad (3.10)$$

ΔC_p will contain sums and differences of all the coefficients a, b and c in (3.7) and may well vary very much less with temperature than any of the individual c_p: its temperature variation has, of course, to be included explicitly in (3.10) before this can be integrated to give an expression for ΔH as a function of temperature.

§ 3.7 The differences between enthalpy and total energy quantities

For molar amounts h and u differ by Pv, which is very small for condensed phases but equal to RT for a perfect gas. If some or all of the participants in a reaction are gases, therefore, ΔH exceeds ΔU by RT multiplied by the number of moles of gas in the products less the number in the reactants. At ordinary temperatures RT is of the order of 600 cal mole^{-1}, while Pv for solids and liquids is only a few thousandths of this. ΔU and ΔH are consequently often very similar, and energy is then the major factor determining an enthalpy change.

§ 3.8 Standard enthalpies

The molar enthalpy of an element or compound in its standard state is known as its standard enthalpy and may be designated $h^\ominus$ or h° if the standard state is the pure substance at 1 atm pressure. The enthalpy change in a reaction between substances all in their standard states, the standard enthalpy change of the reaction, is represented in general by $\Delta H^\ominus$ or by ΔH° if only h° terms are involved. The temperature is also specified: thus $\Delta H^\ominus_{298}$ is the standard enthalpy of a reaction at 25°C. For calculating enthalpy *changes* tables of standard enthalpies of compounds relative to their elements (in their standard states at 1 atm) are very useful: these are called *standard enthalpies of formation*. In such tables the elements naturally appear with the value zero. The enthalpy of any new reaction can then be calculated by adding up the enthalpies of formation of the products and subtracting the sum of the enthalpies of formation of the reactants. (Other extensive properties follow the same pattern. *Do not, therefore, make the mistake of assuming that because ΔG and ΔH are handled similarly in this respect they must be identical. The important difference between them is taken up in the next two chapters.*)

Quite generally, the $\Delta H^\ominus$ values (as the $\Delta G^\ominus$ values) can be added and subtracted along with the corresponding chemical equations. For example, Lewis and Randall point out that although the heat of formation of ethylene is difficult to measure directly,

$$2C \text{ (graphite)} + 2H_2 \text{ (g)} = C_2H_4 \text{ (g)},$$

the ΔH°_{298} of this reaction can be obtained by subtracting the third from the sum of the first two of the following combustion equations:

$$2C \text{ (graphite)} + 2O_2 \text{ (g)} = 2CO_2 \text{ (g)}$$
$$\Delta H^\circ_{298} = -188,104 \text{ cal}$$

$$2H_2 \text{ (g)} \quad + O_2 \text{ (g)} = 2H_2O \text{ (l)}$$
$$\Delta H^\circ_{298} = -136,634 \text{ cal}$$

$$C_2H_4 \ (g) \quad + 3O_2 \ (g) = 2CO_2 \ (g) + 2H_2O \ (l)$$
$$\Delta H°_{298} = -\ 337,230 \ cal$$

$$2C \ (graphite) + 2H_2 \ (g) = C_2H_4 \ (g)$$
$$\Delta H°_{298} = -(188,104 + 136,634)$$
$$-(-337,230) \ cal$$
$$= +12,500 \ cal$$

Confusion often arises with the meaning of 'heat of reaction'. Whereas it is always understood that 'heat of fusion' and 'heat of vaporization' refer to the heat *absorbed* in the phase change, 'heat of reaction' is often taken to mean the heat *evolved*. For this reason it is better to refer explicitly to the ΔH of a reaction: if this is negative, heat is evolved, if positive, heat is absorbed.

§ 3.9 Bond energies

The energy required to break a chemical bond is known as the *bond dissociation energy*. To make sure that the fragments of the molecule really do only dissociate and do not become attached to other molecules or interact in other ways with them, the reaction has to be carried out in the gas phase: e.g.

$$H_2 \ (g) = 2H \ (g) \qquad (3.11)$$

Energies of simple reactions of this kind are usually obtained by molecular spectroscopy, and the results are not only of direct interest in themselves, as measures of the strengths of bonds, but are also used for testing quantum mechanical theories.

From reactions in which several similar bonds are broken, average energies for bonds such as C–H, N–H, O–H, can be determined:

$$CH_4 \ (g) = C \ (g) + 4H \ (g) \qquad (3.12)$$
$$NH_3 \ (g) = N \ (g) + 3H \ (g) \qquad (3.13)$$
$$H_2O \ (g) = O \ (g) + 2H \ (g) \qquad (3.14)$$

41

The energy of each reaction is divided by 4, 3 or 2 respectively for the single bond energy. Each of these reactions is built up by reversing the ordinary formation reaction from the elements and adding equations for the conversion of the elements to the atomic form in the gaseous phase: e.g. to obtain (3.12) add

$$CH_4 \text{ (g)} = C \text{ (s, graphite)} + 2H_2 \text{ (g)} \quad (3.15)$$

$$2H_2 \text{ (g)} = 4H \text{ (g)} \quad (3.16)$$

$$C \text{ (s, graphite)} = C \text{ (g)} \quad (3.17)$$

The energy of (3.15) is obtained calorimetrically (via heats of combustion) and that of (3.16) spectroscopically; but that of the sublimation of graphite, (3.17), has proved very troublesome, and the considerable discrepancies among the published bond energy tables are largely due to the adoption of different values for this quantity. It is now thought to be 170·4 kcal mole^{-1}.

For a useful range of compounds, *bond energies* can be assumed to be almost independent of the compounds in which the bonds occur. Thus, beginning with the value (98 kcal mole^{-1}) determined for C–H from methane, the six C–H bonds in ethane can be allowed for in the energy of atomization of this compound, and the remainder can then be assigned to the C–C bond. In this way, step by step, and taking averages from several compounds where a value can be arrived at in different ways, a whole table of bond energies can be built-up, including values for double bonds, etc. With such a table, rough estimates of heats of formation can often be made, particularly for organic molecules. The sum of all the bond energies of the compound is, of course, an estimate of the energy of its dissociation into atoms. To get to the heat of formation, allowances for the heats of sublimation of carbon, 170·4 kcal mole^{-1}, and of dissociation of hydrogen, 103·2 kcal mole^{-1}, or other diatomic molecules involved, have to be subtracted. Even for organic compounds this additivity rule of bond energies does not hold exactly, for reasons which are often well understood, and more accurate estimates can be made by taking account of some observed regularities in the deviations from additivity.

For the purposes for which bond energies were originally used, values based on $\Delta H°$ data at 25°C were adequate, since thermal effects and the differences between ΔH and ΔU were unimportant. More information has since accumulated for the extrapolation to absolute zero, however, and these extraneous effects are now usually eliminated by referring tables of bond energies to this temperature.

Notice that there is a distinction between a *bond dissociation energy* and an *average bond energy*. There are four different bond dissociation energies for the four stages in which the hydrogen atoms can be separated from carbon in methane (leaving different residual radicals at each stage), although the four C–H bonds in methane itself are equal. The sum of the four stages is, however, equal to four times the C–H bond energy (or approximately so if results for other molecules containing C–H bonds are taken into account to arrive at the most serviceable average value for the tables).

Further work

Read pp. 65–73 and pp. 525–528 in *Thermodynamics*, by G. N. Lewis and M. Randall, 2nd edition revised by K. S. Pitzer and L. Brewer (McGraw-Hill, 1961). See also E. F. Caldin, *Chemical Thermodynamics* (O.U.P., 1958), pp. 40–63.

For the chemical interest of bond energies see L. Pauling, *The Nature of the Chemical Bond*, 3rd edition (Cornell U.P., 1960), and T. L. Cottrell, *The Strength of Chemical Bonds* (Butterworth, 1954).

The estimation of enthalpy quantities in organic chemistry is fully discussed in Chapter 7 of *Estimation of Thermodynamic Properties of Organic Compounds*, by G. J. Janz (Academic Press Inc., 1958).

Problems for Chapter 3

The two books referred to for comparing your answers are:
(L) *Oxidation Potentials*, by W. Latimer (2nd edition, Prentice-Hall Inc., 1952), (B and R) *Thermochemistry of Chemical Substances*, by F. R. Bichowsky and F. D. Rossini (Reinhold, 1936).

1. (*a*) 27 cal are evolved on completely neutralizing 20 ml of 0·1M aqueous HCl with sodium hydroxide. What is ΔH for the reaction

$$H^+ (aq) + OH^- (aq) = H_2O (l)?$$

(*b*) What is ΔH for the ionization of water?

(*c*) What values of ΔH for the ionization of water are assumed in (L) (Table 11, p. 39; see also Table 8, p. 30) and (B and R) p. 20?

2. (*a*) Approximately 80 cal g^{-1} and 540 cal g^{-1} are required to melt ice and to vaporize water respectively. What values for ΔH per mole can be deduced for the fusion of ice and the vaporization of water?

(*b*) Compare your result for the enthalpy of vaporization with the difference between H_2O (g) and H_2O (l) in (L) (Table 11, p. 39) and (B and R) p. 20.

3. (*a*) From the following table of bond energies estimate the enthalpy of formation of liquid ethyl alcohol.

Bond energies in kcal mole^{-1}

C–H	98·2	H–H	103·2
C–C	80·5	O–H	109·4
C–O	79	O=O	117·2

Take the enthalpy of vaporization of alcohol as approximately 10 kcal mole^{-1}.

(Be careful about how many H–H and O=O bonds are involved and take 170·4 kcal mole^{-1} for the enthalpy of sublimation for every g-atom of carbon.)

(*b*) Compare this result with the value recorded in (L), Table 27, p. 128 and (B and R) p. 46.

(*c*) What adjustment to the average C–H bond energy would be required to give exact agreement between the calculated and observed values?

4. Derive integrated equations from (3·6), using (*a*) equation (3·7) and (*b*) equation (3·8) for the temperature dependence of C_p.

4

Energy is not Enough

When a body passes from a higher to a lower gravitational potential without doing work the difference in potential energy appears as kinetic energy which must finally be lost to the surroundings as heat if the temperature of the body is to remain constant. In this particular case the quantity of heat evolved is exactly the same as the work obtainable by carrying out the change reversibly. In other words, the potential energy and total energy changes of the body are the same in changes of this kind; or, ΔU is the quantity which determines the direction of the change.

This simple result tends to prejudice the beginner and to make him ask: How can there be any other factor, apart from the total energy, which can determine the direction of spontaneous change? To weaken this prejudice we now consider a simple chemical reaction which occurs with no energy change at all.

§ 4.1 Spontaneous changes with $\Delta U = 0$

To a very good approximation (except for hydrogen) isotopic atoms differ only in mass and not in chemical properties: the three molecules $^{16}O_2$, $^{18}O_2$ and $^{16}O^{18}O$ have the same bond energy, and any interchange of atoms between them (involving the same number of bonds broken as formed) takes place without significant change of energy.

But if a vessel initially contains only the species $^{16}O_2$ and $^{18}O_2$ in equal numbers the constant interchange of atoms between molecules soon leads to the formation of appreciable amounts of the hybrid species $^{16}O^{18}O$. Perhaps you can guess that the final numbers of $^{16}O_2$, $^{16}O^{18}O$ and $^{18}O_2$ will be in the ratio $1:2:1$.

This simple example shows that a recognizable chemical process can proceed spontaneously without any energy change whatever. Evidently energy cannot be the only factor determining the position of equilibrium. In the case of the reaction

$$^{16}O_2 + {}^{18}O_2 = 2{}^{16}O{}^{18}O \qquad (4.1)$$

the equilibrium constant can even be deduced:

$$K_p = (p\,{}^{16}O^{18}O)^2/p\,{}^{16}O_2 \times p\,{}^{18}O_2 = 2^2/1 \times 1 = 4 \ (4.2)$$

(The partial pressures, p_i, are proportional to the numbers of molecules.)

If this isotopic case seems rather artificial, notice that an effect of exactly this kind, contributing a factor of 4 to the equilibrium constant, always operates in reactions of this pattern, even when the effects of energy changes have also to be taken into account:

$$H_2 \text{ (g)} + Cl_2 \text{ (g)} = 2HCl \text{ (g)} \quad \Delta H^\circ_{298} = -44 \cdot 126 \text{ kcal}$$
$$N_2 \text{ (g)} + O_2 \text{ (g)} = 2NO \text{ (g)} \quad \Delta H^\circ_{298} = +43 \cdot 2 \text{ kcal}$$

(In the formation of HCl the factor of 4 reinforces the effect of the energy change: in the formation of NO it works against the effect of the energy change.)

§ 4.2 Probability

The characteristic feature of this new factor is that it has only to do with numbers, or *probabilities*. The oxygen system just

47

discussed ends with the different species in the ratio $1:2:1$ simply because this is more probable than any other ratio and much more so than the original equimolecular mixture of only two species. Fortunately chemistry is concerned with very large numbers of molecules, and this not only makes virtual certainties of probabilities but also leads to simpler results than would be obtained with small numbers.

For example, with only 4 atoms each of ^{16}O and ^{18}O it would not be very improbable to find all four molecules in the form $^{16}O^{18}O$. For large numbers of molecules, however, when a count is made of all the ways the various possible combinations of numbers of different types of molecules can be built up, it transpires that the $1:2:1$ condition is overwhelmingly more probable than any other and is actually 4^{N_0} (i.e. $K_p{}^{N_0}$) times as probable as the initial equimolecular mixture of only two species for the amount of change represented by equation (4.1): N_0 is the number of molecules in a mole and therefore stands for the number of each of the molecules $^{16}O_2$ and $^{18}O_2$ transformed in the present case. It is always found that, for large numbers, the number of molecules transformed appears as a power in the probability ratio between the initial and final states. The logarithm of this ratio is therefore an extensive property like ΔG, ΔV, etc.

To obtain these results you count up the numbers of different ways the atoms can be grouped to give the specified chemical composition. The relative probabilities of the different chemical compositions are then taken to be proportional to these numbers of ways of grouping the atoms. One way of looking at this is to think of the collection of atoms being reformed continually into pairs quite haphazardly so that all the possible arrangements are explored. The fraction of the time spent in completely homonuclear configurations (only the species $^{16}O_2$ and $^{18}O_2$) then represents the chance of finding the system in that condition compared with that of finding it in the condition where no restrictions as to the molecular species are imposed. To find the 'fraction of the time', you add up the numbers of atomic arrangements which amount to the required chemical description and divide by the total number of arrangements. Like most recipes of this kind, the meaning is much easier to grasp when an actual problem is being tackled, but the method has been outlined in this way to emphasize that *the probability of a state has a precise numerical meaning,* although it may not always be easy to do the actual counting.

Other simple numerical cases, rather like the oxygen isotope reaction, arise from time to time. For example, superimposed upon other effects, a factor of 4 appears in the successive equilibrium constants of a dibasic acid,

$$HOOC \cdot R \cdot COOH + H_2O = HOOC \cdot R \cdot COO^- + H_3O^+$$
$$HOOC \cdot R \cdot COO^- + H_2O = {}^-OOC \cdot R \cdot COO^- + H_3O^+$$

because there are two sites from which the first acid can lose protons and two sites at which the second base can gain them. A slightly more complicated case of the same kind arises in the successive addition of ligands to a central metal ion, such as the successive addition of four NH_3 molecules to Cu^{2+}, for example.

But the probability effects so far mentioned are only of importance in special cases. *Two other kinds of distribution are much more generally important: these are the distribution of energy among molecules and the distribution of molecules in space.* Although the actual counting may be rather more troublesome, both kinds of distribution are fundamentally determined by the laws of chance and involve comparisons of probabilities in the same precise way as before. That is, when *all* the different factors have been taken into account a definite number, say $\mathscr{P}$, can be assigned to the probability of a given state, relative to an agreed standard state, and there will be a natural tendency for the system to change to states with higher $\mathscr{P}$ values. ($\mathscr{P}$ is conveniently kept as a *relative* probability and can therefore be a large number: it does not have to be less than unity like a normalized, or absolute, probability.)

49

§ 4.3 Probability and work

Although a process like (4.1) involves no change of energy, being spontaneous, it can still in principle be harnessed to yield work according to the work rule. Consider now two successive changes of this kind, from $\mathscr{P}_1$ to $\mathscr{P}_2$ and then from $\mathscr{P}_2$ to $\mathscr{P}_3$, associated with (maximum) available work W'_{12} for the first change and W'_{23} for the second. Reflection on the same overall change $\mathscr{P}_1$ to $\mathscr{P}_3$ carried out in a single stage then shows that, while the probabilities are compounded by multiplication, the work terms are compounded by addition:

$$\mathscr{P}_2/\mathscr{P}_1 \times \mathscr{P}_3/\mathscr{P}_2 = \mathscr{P}_3/\mathscr{P}_1 \qquad (4.3)$$

$$W'_{12} + W'_{23} = W'_{13} \qquad (4.4)$$

The work terms must therefore be proportional to the logarithms of the probability ratios:

$$W'_{ij} = \theta \ln (\mathscr{P}_j/\mathscr{P}_i), \qquad (4.5)$$

where θ is a proportionality factor.

Figure 4.1 may help to make the idea of harnessing a process like (4.1) more acceptable.

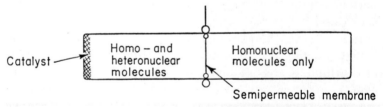

FIG. 4.1

Imagine that (a) a certain reaction of this type requires a catalyst, without which no change occurs, and (b) a membrane is available which is permeable to homonuclear but not to heteronuclear molecules. This membrane operates as a piston, the motion of which can be harnessed magnetically (as in Figure 2.1). With the piston at first next to the catalyst on the left wall of the vessel in Figure 4.1, homonuclear molecules from the initial mixture on the right can penetrate the membrane, react at the catalyst and push the piston to the right by the excess pressure of the heteronuclear species formed. The partial pressure of each homonuclear species will tend to equalize on each side of the membrane, whatever the other species present, by (2.9).

§ 4.4 Probability and heat

When a change such as (4.1) proceeds without being harnessed to do work there is no alteration in the energy. Therefore, according to the definition of total energy changes (3.1), when the same process is carried out reversibly so that the maximum work is done, *the energy for this work must be absorbed from outside as heat if the same final state is to be arrived at.* (Otherwise the temperature would have to drop.) This gives the clue to a very important way of measuring probability changes in chemical processes: the work available from a probability change, (4.5), can always be measured by the heat absorbed when the change is carried out reversibly. This applies whether there is an accompanying change in the energy or not. (See § 5.8.)

§ 4.5 The absolute temperature scale

Does the maximum work, (4.5), obtainable from the oxygen reaction, (4.1), depend upon the temperature? It is not perhaps immediately obvious that it should do, since no temperature has so far been specified and the number $\mathscr{P}_2/\mathscr{P}_1$ has only been related to the probability of encountering the three species in the ratio $1:2:1$ compared with that of finding only the homonuclear species present; so $\mathscr{P}_2/\mathscr{P}_1$ is independent of the temperature in that case. If there is any temperature dependence of W'_{12} therefore it must reside in the proportionality factor θ of equation (4.5).

Imagine a process like (4.1), depending only on numbers, to

take place reversibly at two temperatures, in the spontaneous direction at the upper temperature and in the opposite direction at the lower temperature. Call the factor θ_H at the higher temperature and θ_L at the lower.

Now consider a completed cycle

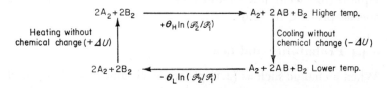

The two stages labelled 'cooling' and 'heating' must cancel exactly in their heat and work contributions to the whole cycle, since by hypothesis there is to be no energy change in the reaction at either temperature, and this ensures that the ΔU for the heating and cooling stages must be equal and opposite. If no work is done at all in these stages (constant volume) the heat contributions must also be equal and opposite. Even if these stages are carried out at constant pressure, the $P\Delta V$ work terms, and hence the heat terms, still cancel for a reaction like (4.1), since there is no change in the number of molecules.

By starting at the top left-hand corner and following the directions of the arrows, a cycle can be completed in which the work done is $(\theta_H - \theta_L) \ln (\mathscr{P}_2/\mathscr{P}_1)$, the difference (if any) between that done *by* the system at the higher temperature and that done *on* the system at the lower, each calculated according to (4.5). But heat equivalent to $\theta_H \ln (\mathscr{P}_2/\mathscr{P}_1)$ has to be absorbed from the surroundings at the higher temperature when the change occurs reversibly, as explained in § 4.4; and similarly $\theta_L \ln (\mathscr{P}_2/\mathscr{P}_1)$ has to be given up to the surroundings at the lower temperature. On balance, therefore, the heat $\theta_L \ln (\mathscr{P}_2/\mathscr{P}_1)$ is transferred from a higher to a lower temperature, the extra heat absorbed at the higher temperature, $(\theta_H - \theta_L) \ln (\mathscr{P}_2/\mathscr{P}_1)$, being converted to the work (if any) produced in the cycle.

But the passage of heat from a higher to a lower temperature is a spontaneous process and, by the work rule, can be made to yield work when harnessed (as in heat engines). Yet this precisely summarizes the net effect of the cycle. Hence the work $(\theta_H - \theta_L) \ln (\mathscr{P}_2/\mathscr{P}_1)$ must be positive: i.e. $\theta_H > \theta_L$, or the constant of equation (4.5) is greater at the higher temperature. (You may be more convinced by working the cycle the other way round, so that heat is transferred from the lower to the higher temperature and θ_H has to be greater than θ_L to account for the necessary work done *on* the system against the natural direction of heat flow.) In other words, due to its fundamental property of determining the direction of heat flow, the temperature must logically affect the value of θ.

The ratio of the work done by the system in the cycle to the heat absorbed at the higher temperature is $(\theta_H - \theta_L)/\theta_H$ and involves only θ_H and θ_L, since the logarithmic term cancels out. This ratio is a measure of the efficiency of the system regarded as a device for producing work from heat, and according to *Carnot's theorem* (see problem 4) its value must be the same for *all* reversible cycles working between the same temperatures, independently of the nature of the substances involved. It follows that the ratio θ_H/θ_L also depends only upon the temperatures involved and that θ values for different substances always increase in the same proportion to one another as the temperature is increased. This provides a natural basis for an *absolute temperature scale*, since any quantity proportional to θ would serve as a common temperature scale for all substances, always increasing as the temperature increases and uniquely determining the extent of the reversible conversion of heat into work between two temperatures.

§ 4.6 Probability and temperature in the isothermal expansion of a perfect gas

Consider a mole (N_0 molecules) of a perfect gas expanding isothermally from a volume v_1 to a volume v_2. Since there are no forces between the molecules of a perfect gas, the inter-molecular potential energies are quite unchanged in the expansion and the total energy of the gas is the same at the end as at the beginning of the operation. Yet there is no doubting the tendency of the gas to expand into a large volume whenever this is made available, despite the fact that no energy change is involved. In molecular terms, when the larger volume v_2 is available, it would be extremely unlikely to find all the N_0 molecules confined to the original volume v_1 rather than spread randomly throughout the system. This happens to be a case where the ratio $\mathscr{P}_2/\mathscr{P}_1$ can be calculated rather easily.

For the chance of finding a particular molecule in the original restricted sector v_1 rather than anywhere in the total volume v_2 is simply v_1/v_2 and, since the molecules of a perfect gas are quite independent of one another, the chance of finding two molecules together in v_1 is $(v_1/v_2) \times (v_1/v_2)$, as any situation of the first molecule imposes no restriction on the second. But the same applies to all the molecules, and hence the probability of finding them all in v_1 rather than anywhere in v_2 is $(v_1/v_2)^{N_0}$, and this contributes to $\mathscr{P}_1/\mathscr{P}_2$.

Since the temperature does not change, all other contributions to $\mathscr{P}$ for the two states are quite unaffected, and therefore

$$\mathscr{P}_2/\mathscr{P}_1 = (v_2/v_1)^{N_0} \qquad (4.6)$$

and the work available when the tendency to expand is harnessed must be given by (4.5) as

$$W'_{12} = \theta \ln (\mathscr{P}_2/\mathscr{P}_1) = N_0\theta \ln (v_2/v_1) \qquad (4.7)$$

But the maximum work of expansion can also be calculated from $\int P dv$ using $Pv = RT$:

$$W'_{12} = \int_{v_1}^{v_2} P dv = RT \int_{v_1}^{v_2} dv/v = RT \ln (v_2/v_1) \qquad (4.8)$$

Comparison of (4.7) with (4.8) then yields the extremely convenient result

$$\theta = RT/N_0 = kT \qquad (4.9)$$

where k is R/N_0, the gas constant per molecule. This means that the gas scale of temperature already has the property (proportionality to θ) required of an absolute scale and can therefore be used to anchor it numerically. To make the degree the same size as the degree Centigrade the normal freezing-point of water is set at $273 \cdot 15°K$, the $°K$ standing for degrees on the Kelvin (absolute) scale.

At the macroscopic level two bodies are in thermal equilibrium when they have the same temperature T. But at the molecular level, when the counting is done for the distribution of kinetic energy among the molecules, it transpires that it is θ which has to be equalized for thermal equilibrium. This means that θ must be the same for all substances for a fixed temperature, which may seem reasonable enough, since the $\mathscr{P}$ terms in (4.5) are simply numbers and the tendency to change from one probability number to another could therefore be expected to be independent of the nature of the process. Since θ is equal to kT for an ideal gas, it must therefore be equal to kT quite generally for all substances, and k, which always connects the 'statistical temperature' θ with the 'thermodynamic temperature' T, must be a universal constant. It is known as *Boltzmann's constant* and has the value $1 \cdot 38045 \times 10^{-16}$ erg deg^{-1}.

Equation (4.5) can now be written

$$W'_{12} = kT \ln (\mathscr{P}_2/\mathscr{P}_1) \qquad (4.10)$$

§ 4.7 Entropy

The logarithm of $\mathscr{P}$ is extensive because $\mathscr{P}$ always contains the number of molecules as a power. (See § 4.2 and compare equations (4.6) and (4.7).) This logarithmic form crops up as soon as the probability is related to work, heat and energy and is so useful that it has a special name: $k \ln \mathscr{P}$ is known as the *entropy* and is represented by the symbol S.

$$S = k \ln \mathscr{P} \qquad (4.11)$$

For the change from state 1 to state 2,

$$\Delta S_{12} = S_2 - S_1 = k \ln \mathscr{P}_2 - k \ln \mathscr{P}_1 = k \ln (\mathscr{P}_2/\mathscr{P}_1) \quad (4.12)$$

which is W'_{12} divided by the temperature (W'_{12} being the contribution to the maximum work available due to the entropy change, as given by (4.10)), or Q/T. Q is the heat absorbed when the entropy change is carried out reversibly and T is the temperature at which it is absorbed.

It has already been emphasized that a definite number $\mathscr{P}$ can be assigned to a given state, and so S must also depend only upon the state of a system. This means that whenever a complete cycle of operations is performed, restoring the system to its original state, the entropy changes *of the system* for all the stages of the cycle must add up to zero, just as is the case for the sum of the total energy changes.

Now this is not true of the heat changes in a reversible cycle, because some of the heat is transformed into work. In the cycle described above, the heat changes in the 'heating' and 'cooling' stages cancel, but the heat absorbed at the higher temperature can now be written as $kT_H \ln (\mathscr{P}_2/\mathscr{P}_1)$ and that emitted at the lower temperature as $kT_L \ln (\mathscr{P}_2/\mathscr{P}_1)$ and these are not equal. The corresponding *entropy* changes do, however, cancel, being of magnitude $k \ln (\mathscr{P}_2/\mathscr{P}_1)$ and equal and opposite. Thus dividing Q, the heat absorbed reversibly at every stage, by T, the temperature at which it is absorbed, transforms the heat into a function of the state of the system.

Dividing Q by T would always give a state function even if the proportionality constant between θ and T had not turned out to be equal to k for all systems, and changes in the 'thermodynamic entropy' are defined by the relation

$$dS = dQ/T \qquad (4.13)$$

(dS is the small entropy change associated with the absorption of the small amount of heat dQ at the temperature T under reversible conditions.)

(4.11) is said to define the 'statistical entropy'. This does not mean that there are two different types of entropy: one is merely an explanation of the other in terms of a consistent statistical theory. If you want to measure entropy changes use (4.13); if you want to understand them think of (4.11).

§ 4.8 Entropy changes in chemical reactions

Entropy is another extensive state function like G, U, H and V, and tables can therefore be drawn up of the molar entropies of chemical compounds in their standard states, and these quantities can be added and subtracted just like molar free energies and enthalpies. The standard ΔS for a reaction is calculated from such tables along familiar lines:

$$\Delta S^{\ominus} = \left(\sum_i \nu_i s^{\ominus}_i\right)_{\text{products}} - \left(\sum_i \nu_i s^{\ominus}_i\right)_{\text{reactants}} \quad (4.14)$$

This entropy increase in a chemical reaction is quite as definite as the increase in volume, and when a definite chemical reaction takes place in a beaker the entropy increase within the beaker is fixed by equation (4.14) whether the change takes place reversibly or not, provided of course that the same final conditions of temperature, pressure and concentration are reached.

§ 4.9 A very important equation

For an isothermal process, the work available on harnessing the tendency to change due to an entropy increase is $T\Delta S$, as can be seen by comparing (4.10) and (4.12).

But this chapter began with an example of a change in which the work obtainable from harnessing an energy decrease is simply $-\Delta U$ (a positive quantity when ΔU is negative).

57

Assuming for the present that *the total work from a process involving both energy and entropy changes* is simply obtained by adding the two contributions together,

$$W = -\Delta U + T\Delta S$$

If the process is carried out at constant pressure the $P\Delta V$ work is unavailable and the *available work* W' (equal to $-\Delta G$ by (1.4)) is given by

$$W' = W - P\Delta V = -(\Delta U + P\Delta V) + T\Delta S = -\Delta H + T\Delta S.$$

Hence $$\Delta G = \Delta H - T\Delta S \tag{4.15}$$

for an *isothermal* process.

Since G, H and S are all state functions, this equation can be applied immediately to the special case of the standard changes in these quantities when the products and reactants are in their standard states:

$$\Delta G° = \Delta H° - T\Delta S° \tag{4.16}$$

(or, more generally, $\Delta G^{\ominus} = \Delta H^{\ominus} - T\Delta S^{\ominus}$).

To assess the tendency for chemical changes to occur you therefore have to take account of both the energy and the entropy factors involved. These factors may reinforce or oppose one another, but one generalization emerges at once from the way the temperature appears in the equation: at very low temperatures energy dominates entropy in fixing the position of equilibrium, but the entropy factor becomes more and more important as the temperature is increased.

Equation (4.16) forms the basis for the estimation of $\Delta G°$, and hence of chemical equilibrium constants, from thermal data alone: given the thermal quantities $\Delta H°$ and $\Delta S°$, $\Delta G°$ can always be calculated.

Remembering the important connexion between $\Delta G°$ and equilibrium constants, equation (2.14), we see that the practical determination of a single equilibrium constant does not distinguish between the energy and entropy factors which go to make up $\Delta G°$ but only indicates their net result. Now look again at the simple reaction (4.1), for which $\Delta U° - 0$, $\Delta V° = 0$, i.e. $\Delta H° = 0$, and for which we guessed $K_p = 4$ from probability ideas alone. In that case, $\Delta G° = -RT \ln 4$, determined entirely by the entropy factor.

§ 4.10 A paradox

At the beginning of this chapter the question was: 'How can there be any other factor, apart from the total energy, which can determine the direction of spontaneous change?' But after reading § 4.2 you may well be wondering instead 'How can any factor other than the *entropy* determine the direction of spontaneous change?' For, once understood, the drift towards states of higher probability seems to leave no room for any other factor at all. In effect, it may appear that clarifying the role of entropy has only made that of energy more obscure.

This paradox is resolved at the end of the next chapter, where a proper justification of equation (4.15) is also given. Basically, the point is that $\Delta S°$ in (4.16) only measures the entropy change within the system of interest, while $\Delta H°$ accounts for the entropy change of the surroundings.

Further work

Read the article on 'entropy and probability' in Lewis and Randall's *Thermodynamics* (McGraw-Hill, 1923), pp. 120–128. In Pitzer and Brewer's revised edition (1961) it occurs as Chapter 8, pp. 87–93.

Problems for Chapter 4

1. Calculate $\Delta G°_{298}$ and $\Delta G°_{1,000}$ for reaction (4.1).

2. (a) For the reaction

$$Pb\ (s) + 2AgCl\ (s) = PbCl_2\ (s) + 2Ag\ (s)$$

$\Delta H°_{298}$ is $-25 \cdot 126$ kcal.

This chemical reaction is harnessed in a cell and the e.m.f. is found to be $0 \cdot 4900$ volt at $25°C$. How much heat is absorbed during the reversible working of the cell?

(b) Calculate $\Delta H°_{298}$, $\Delta G°_{298}$ and $\Delta S°_{298}$ for this reaction from the data given in (L), pp. 152 and 190. (Note that Latimer uses $\Delta F°$ for $\Delta G°$.)

3. From the following data calculate $\Delta H^{\ominus}_{298}$, $\Delta G^{\ominus}_{298}$ and $\Delta S^{\ominus}_{298}$ for the reaction

$$CH_3COOH\ (aq) = CH_3COO^-\ (aq) + H^+\ (aq)$$

Standard enthalpies and free energies of formation (in kcal):

	$\Delta H^{\ominus}$	$\Delta G^{\ominus}$
H^+ (aq)	$0 \cdot 0$	$0 \cdot 0$
CH_3COO^- (aq)	$-116 \cdot 843$	$-89 \cdot 02$
CH_3COOH (aq)	$-116 \cdot 743$	$-95 \cdot 51$

Calculate the equilibrium constant for the reaction and comment upon the importance or otherwise of the entropy factor in determining the position of equilibrium in this case.

4. For the cycle in § 4.5, the ratio of the work done by the system to the heat absorbed at the higher temperature is $(\theta_H - \theta_L)/\theta_H$. If the cycle is worked the other way round (as in a refrigerator) it is seen that the ratio of the heat delivered at the higher temperature to the work done *on* the system is $\theta_H/(\theta_H - \theta_L)$.

Now consider two cycles, using different working substances but operating reversibly between the same temperatures, coupled so that all the work (W_1) from one is used to drive the other backwards ($W_2 = -W_1$). Apply the work rule to the overall effects of the coupled cycles to show that the heat delivered at the upper temperature by the second cycle, $|Q_2|$, cannot exceed the heat absorbed at the upper temperature by the first, Q_1. (The heat exchanged at the lower temperature is in each case equal to the difference between the work done and the heat exchanged at the higher temperature.)

Since the roles of the two cycles may be interchanged, show that the ratios W_1/Q_1 and W_2/Q_2 must be equal, and hence that *all* reversible cycles operating between the same two temperatures must have the efficiency $(\theta_H - \theta_L)/\theta_H$, whether the isothermal process involves a characteristic energy change or not. (Carnot's theorem.)

5

Entropy

§ 5.1 Quantum theory and the meaning of $\mathscr{P}$

Atoms and molecules exist only in quantum states of definite energies determined by the rules of quantum mechanics. It sometimes happens that for a given atom (or molecule) the energies of ω recognizably different quantum states turn out to be the same, and these quantum states are then said to belong to an *energy level* of *degeneracy* ω (e.g. the p-type atomic orbitals). This increases ω-fold the chance of finding an atom in this particular energy level compared with a 'singlet' energy level: the energy level has a 'probability weight' of ω.

Now a system composed of many molecules is also subject to the rules of quantum mechanics, and it, too, has quantum states and energy levels. For such a system in a specified condition, the 'energy level' is simply its total energy, while its degeneracy is given by the number of quantum states of the system corresponding to this energy. A quantum state of the system as a whole is a combination of the quantum states of the individual molecules, and each recognizably different combination of these is a different quantum state of the system. The degeneracy of a large collection of molecules can be very large indeed, since the molecules can be arranged among the many energy levels available to them in a very large number of ways without any change in the overall sum of their energies. Just as for a single atom, this degeneracy gives the probability weight for the given energy level of the whole system; but this is exactly what is meant by $\mathscr{P}$. In quantum mechanical language therefore, $\mathscr{P}$ *is simply defined as the number of quantum states corresponding to a given energy of the system* which is equivalent to the number of recognizably different ways in which the total energy can be distributed. (It is sometimes represented by the symbols Ω or W in books on statistical mechanics.) This definition of $\mathscr{P}$ covers all types of distribution, including the distribution of molecules in space.

It is as well to be aware of this correspondence between molecules and whole systems in regard to numbers of quantum states when reading more advanced books on this subject, since some very important conclusions about distributions among quantum states apply equally well both to systems composed of large numbers of similar molecules and to imaginary assemblies composed of large numbers of similar macroscopic systems.

§ 5.2 The distribution of molecules among energy levels

An easily understandable case of the partition of energy among molecules is that of the distribution of translational kinetic energy. The molecules in a gas are constantly colliding with each other at all sorts of angles, and at each collision their kinetic energy can be redistributed in a variety of ways: it can be almost completely taken by one of the molecules, leaving the other practically at rest, or the two molecules may bounce apart with practically the same energy as they had before the collision. Evidently there must be a wide range of molecular kinetic energies in a gas at any instant, although with very large numbers of molecules one would expect the average number with a given energy to remain constant in time if the gas is at equilibrium. The necessary calculation was done by Maxwell, and his argument was extended and generalized by Boltzmann.

In quantum mechanical terms, *Boltzmann's distribution law* is as follows. Let N_1', N_2', N_3', ... denote the numbers of molecules in the quantum states with energies ϵ_1', ϵ_2', ϵ_3', ... Then

$$N_1' : N_2' : N_3' : \ldots = e^{-\epsilon_1'/kT} : e^{-\epsilon_2'/kT} : e^{-\epsilon_3'/kT} : \ldots \quad (5.1)$$

The distribution covers all quantum states and all molecules; so for a given pure substance $\Sigma N_i' = N$, the total number of molecules, and $\Sigma \epsilon_i' = U$, the total energy.

When quantum states have the same energy they are grouped together as degenerate states of the same energy level. In terms of energy levels rather than quantum states, it therefore follows immediately from (5.1), by setting the ϵ_i equal in groups of ω_i, that

$$N_1 : N_2 : N_3 : \ldots = \omega_1 e^{-\epsilon_1/kT} : \omega_2 e^{-\epsilon_2/kT} : \omega_3 e^{\epsilon_3/kT} \ldots \quad (5.2)$$

Here the unprimed N_1, N_2, N_3, ... refer to the numbers of molecules in the respective energy levels. As the temperature is increased and the ϵ_i/kT exponents decrease towards zero, $N_1 : N_2 : N_3 \ldots$ tends towards $\omega_1 : \omega_2 : \omega_3 : \ldots$; but the numbers of molecules in the lower levels still fall off because levels of higher ϵ become appreciably populated (N_i, the number of molecules in the ith level, is always obtainable from the factor $\omega_i \exp(-\epsilon_i/kT)$ by dividing by the sum of all such factors, $\sum_i \omega_i \exp(-\epsilon_i/kT)$. This sum, which must increase with increasing temperature, is called a *partition function* and is important in statistical mechanics because of its relationship to free energy.)

Even at this stage the correspondence between 'macro' and 'micro' systems may help in grasping the significance of the form of (5.2). For it gives directly a value for such a ratio as N_1/N_2 (which is rather like a simple equilibrium constant) as

$(\omega_2/\omega_1) \exp [-(\epsilon_2 - \epsilon_1)/kT]$; or, after taking logarithms and multiplying by $-kT$,

$$-kT \ln (N_2/N_1) = (\epsilon_2 - \epsilon_1) - kT \ln (\omega_2/\omega_1) \quad (5.3)$$

This is very reminiscent of the equation $\Delta G = \Delta H - T\Delta S$, and shows that at the molecular level also the equilibrium distributions are determined by energy and probability factors related in the same way as for macroscopic systems.

§ 5.3 Boltzmann's law and entropy

Relative to the lowest energy level, the numbers of molecules in the higher levels fall off exponentially with the ratio ϵ/kT (apart from the ω factor). Electronic energy levels are the most widely spaced, and for most molecules at about room temperature ϵ/kT is 100 or more for just the first transition (O_2 and NO are prominent exceptions). The higher electronic levels are therefore extremely sparsely populated at ordinary temperatures and might just as well not be there as far as their effect on molecular distribution is concerned. Vibrational levels are the next most widely spaced and have ϵ/kT of the order of a few units, while rotational spacings are about a thousand times smaller and translational spacings very much smaller still.

The relevance of this law to the understanding of entropy is this. *The closer the spacing of the molecular energy levels, the greater the number of quantum states available to the system as a whole and the greater its entropy.* From this simple rule some very important qualitative deductions about molar entropies can be made.

Fortunately it can nearly always be assumed that the effects of vibration, rotation and translation can be treated quite separately, the idea being that any particular vibrational state, for example, can be combined with the same sets of rotational and translational states as any other. (This cannot be strictly true, since the interatomic distances, and hence moments of inertia, would be affected slightly in a vibrational energy

65

change for an anharmonic vibrator, and hence the rotational levels would also be affected.) The consequence is that the effects of these different forms of motion on the entropy are additive (really because exp $[-(\epsilon_{vib} + \epsilon_{rot} + \epsilon_{trans})/kT]$ can be factorized into three terms before taking logarithms). For perfect gases and solids it is usually clear how to classify the various forms of motion, but even with imperfect gases and liquids, where intermolecular forces come into play, the internal motions of the molecules are often hardly affected by these forces and can be treated as independent.

From the spacing of the energy levels (translational spacing closer than rotational, which is closer than vibrational) it follows that the entropy contributions from translational motion are more important than those from rotational motion and much more important than those from vibrational motion.

§ 5.4 Entropy and temperature

However the energies are classified, the ratio ϵ/kT always diminishes with increasing temperature so that more levels become available for significant population and the number of quantum states increases. Thus the *entropy increases with temperature*.

Figure 5.1 gives an impression of the way temperature affects the distribution of molecules among the same set of non-degenerate levels. As ϵ/kT becomes smaller (with increasing temperature), the Boltzmann factors exp $(-\epsilon/kT)$ approach unity and all levels of the same degeneracy tend to become equally populated. (In many cases of chemical interest, the degeneracy of the levels actually increases with increasing energy, and this has the effect of introducing a maximum into the population diagram, as in Figure 5.2.)

If energy is simply added as heat to a system at equilibrium it becomes distributed among the molecules in a way that brings about a slight change from (say) the low-temperature distribution of Figure 5.1 or 5.2 towards the high-temperature distribution. In this way, the increments, $c\,dT$, of heat added

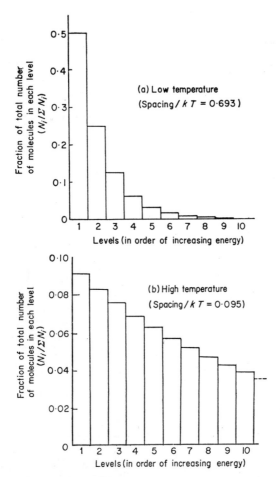

FIG. 5.1 Temperature effect upon the population of energy levels with equal spacing and $\omega_i = 1$

account for both the increase in energy and, when divided by the temperature at which they are absorbed, for the increase in entropy (see equation (4.13)).

67

For conditions of constant volume,

$$\int du = \int c_v \, dT; \quad \int ds = \int c_v \, dT/T = \int c_v \, d\ln T \quad (5.4)$$

For conditions of constant pressure,

$$\int dh = \int c_p \, dT; \quad \int ds = \int c_p \, dT/T = \int c_p \, d\ln T \quad (5.5)$$

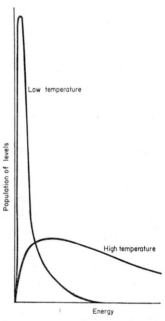

FIG. 5.2   Temperature effect upon the population of energy levels
with very close spacing and ω increasing with energy

Apart from the entropy changes associated with latent heat, these formulae suffice for the calculation of the entropy of a substance at some specified temperature (such as 298°K) relative to its value at some very low temperature, and in particular, if some reliable method of extrapolation can be devised, relative to its value at 0°K. The molar heat capacities, c_p, of many substances have been determined down to below 20°K, and the short final extrapolation has been made for solids by using the proportionality of c_p to T^3 deduced theoretically.

At the absolute zero of temperature all molecules are in their lowest energy states only, and most substances have these molecules arranged in a perfectly ordered lattice. Since all the molecules of a pure substance are identical, such a condition is only describable by one quantum state. Hence the entropy, which depends upon the logarithm of the number of quantum states, is zero. Entropies at other temperatures calculated with reference to o°K can therefore be said to be on an absolute scale.

A little qualification is necessary; certain sources of disorder, such as isotopic mixing and nuclear effects, can only be studied and eliminated at 1°K or below, and are therefore not accounted for in the usual extrapolation from somewhat higher temperatures. Since the temperatures involved are so small, even quite small energy changes can correspond to appreciable entropy (Q/T) terms, but for chemical purposes there is no disadvantage in ignoring (constant) effects of this kind and taking the extrapolated entropy as zero, since they would always cancel out in any chemical application. Residual disorder effects of rather a different kind do, however, show up in a few special cases and then have to be taken into account in detailed work. (They may arise either from 'freezing-in' a distribution corresponding to equilibrium at some higher temperature or from some inherent degeneracy associated with the lowest energy level of the molecules, or a structural freak, like that of ice, which has alternative positions for the hydrogen bonds in its crystal lattice.)

The contrast between the low entropy of a perfectly ordered crystalline lattice and the high entropy of a gas emphasizes the important correlation between entropy and disorder or randomness.

§ 5.5 Entropy and latent heat

Heat is absorbed when a liquid is vaporized, but equilibrium is possible between the liquid and its vapour because the increase in potential associated with this increase in energy can be exactly balanced by the decrease in potential associated with the accompanying increase in entropy. A pure liquid boils when its vapour pressure reaches atmospheric pressure, and under the conditions of this constant pressure it absorbs the latent heat l_v per mole (the ΔH of the process) at the boiling-point T_b (in °K). Since there is equilibrium between the liquid and the vapour, ΔG is zero for the passage of a mole between the two phases, whence $\Delta H = T\Delta S$, or $\Delta s = l_v/T_b$, the *molar entropy of vaporization*.

Similarly, the *molar entropy of fusion* is l_f/T_f, the molar heat of fusion divided by the freezing temperature in °K and the molar entropy change for a transition from one crystalline form to another at T_t is l_t/T_t (l_t is the molar heat of the transition).

§ 5.6 Standard entropies

These l/T terms have to be taken into account along with the results of (5.5) to arrive at the total molar entropy of a substance at a given temperature. For example, the entropy at 298°K of HCl gas is the sum of the results of the following steps:

(1) By extrapolation from 16°K to 0°K $\qquad \Delta s_1 = 0\cdot30$ e.u.

(2) $\int c_p \mathrm{d}\ln T$ from 16° to 98·36° for solid$_{\mathrm{I}}$ $\Delta s_2 = 7\cdot06$ e.u.

(3) Solid transition, 284·3/98·36 e.u. $\qquad \Delta s_3 = 2\cdot89$ e.u.

(4) $\int c_p \mathrm{d}\ln T$ from 98·36° to 158·91°K for solid$_{\mathrm{II}}$

$\qquad\qquad\qquad\qquad\qquad\qquad\qquad \Delta s_4 = 5\cdot05$ e.u.

(5) $l_f/T_f = 476\cdot0/158\cdot91$ e.u., fusion $\qquad \Delta s_5 = 3\cdot00$ e.u.

(6) $\int c_p \mathrm{d}\ln T$ from 158·91° to 188·07°K for liquid

$\qquad\qquad\qquad\qquad\qquad\qquad\qquad \Delta s_6 = 2\cdot36$ e.u.

(7) $l_v/T_v = 3860/188 \cdot 07$ e.u., vaporization $\Delta s_7 = 20 \cdot 52$ e.u.

(8) $\int c_p \mathrm{d} \ln T$ from $188 \cdot 07°$ to $298 \cdot 15°K$ for gas

$$\Delta s_8 = 3 \cdot 22 \text{ e.u.}$$

Hence $s°_{298}$ for HCl = $\qquad$ 44·4 e.u.

(See W. F. Giauque and R. Wiebe, *J. Amer. Chem. Soc.*, 1928, **50**, 101.)

The abbreviation e.u. stands for cal deg^{-1} mole^{-1}, the 'entropy unit'.

The standard entropies of the elements are also referred to $0°K$ in the same way. This explains why it is that in tables of standard thermodynamic properties (like those in Latimer's *Oxidation Potentials*) the entropies of the elements are not zero, unlike the free energies and enthalpies: $\Delta g°_{298}$ and $\Delta h°_{298}$ are free energies and enthalpies of formation, relative to the elements, while the $s°_{298}$ for all substances are absolute entropies referred to the zero at $0°K$.

In some books, however, the functions $-(g° - h°_{298})/T$ or $-(g° - h°_0)/T$ are tabulated at various temperatures instead of the separate $\Delta g°$, $\Delta h°$ and $s°_{298}$ values. These composite functions represent free energies (divided by the temperature) relative to the enthalpy either at $298°K$ or at $0°K$, and are useful because they facilitate the calculation of equilibrium constants over a wide range of temperature. Standard entropies can be calculated from such tables with the help of the formula $g° = h° - Ts°$:

$$s°_{298} = [-(g° - h°_{298})/T]_{298} \qquad (5.6)$$
$$= [-(g° - h°_0)/T]_{298} + (h°_{298} - h°_0)/298 \cdot 15 \quad (5.7)$$

For example, Pitzer and Brewer's table (Lewis and Randall, *Thermodynamics*, 2nd edition, McGraw-Hill, p. 680) has under I_2 (s) the value $17 \cdot 18$ e.u. at $298°K$ for $-(g° - h°_0)/T$ and $3 \cdot 154$ kcal mole^{-1} for $(h°_{298} - h°_0)$: $\Delta h°_0$, the enthalpy of formation at $0°K$ from the element in its common form, is of course zero. By $(5\cdot7)$,

$$s°_{298} = 17\cdot18 + 3,154/298\cdot15 \text{ or } \underline{27\cdot74} \text{ e.u.}$$

§ 5·7 The entropies of gases

A glance at the stages in the determination of the entropy of HCl in § 5.6 shows that by far the largest single contribution (almost half the total entropy) comes from the entropy of vaporization. This is not surprising, since molecules have much greater freedom for translational motion in a gas than in a condensed phase, and translational energy levels are very closely spaced. According to the quantum theory, in a rectangular box of dimensions a × b × c the translational energy states available to a molecule of mass m are

$$\epsilon = \frac{h^2}{8m}\left(\frac{n_x^2}{a^2} + \frac{n_y^2}{b^2} + \frac{n_z^2}{c^2}\right) \qquad (5.8)$$

where n_x, n_y, n_z are integers and h is Planck's constant. It follows immediately that the spacing is reduced, and hence the entropy is increased, by an increase of the molecular mass. (Observe that the degeneracy, ω, of translational levels increases with the energy because of the possible combinations of the three numbers n_x^2, n_y^2, n_z^2 in the formula. An important temperature-dependent maximum therefore occurs in the energy distribution: see Figure 5.2.)

By the methods of statistical mechanics the translational entropy corresponding to the energy spacing (5.8) turns out to be

$$s_{tr} = R\left[\ln \frac{(2\pi mkT)^{3/2} v}{h^3 N_0} + 5/2\right] \qquad (5.9)$$

which shows that, other things being equal, the entropy actually increases with the mass as $(3R/2)\ln m$, and also with the volume v as $R \ln v$. This last result is in agreement with (4.8).

72

From the chemical point of view, this high entropy of gases means that reactions involving the production of gases from liquids and solids are accompanied by an increase in entropy, as are dissociation reactions in the gas phase, such as

$$I_2 \text{ (g)} = 2I \text{ (g)} \qquad (5.10)$$

Since the effects of entropy outweigh those of energy at high temperatures, this implies that polyatomic molecules will tend to break up into atoms at high temperatures, just as you would expect.

Monatomic gases have only translational motion, and therefore provide a perfect test of (5.9). Remember that this is a theoretical equation based on statistical reasoning, while the procedure for the experimental determination of s°_{298} calorimetrically is outlined in § 5.6. Yet for the rare gases, which have s°_{298} values at 30–40 e.u., the 'calorimetric' and 'statistical' entropies agree to about 0·1 e.u. This is a most remarkable verification of a considerable body of thermodynamic theory.

Similar success has been obtained with more complex gaseous molecules, for which the statistical translational contribution has to be supplemented by rotational and (less important) vibrational contributions. These require knowledge of the shapes and vibration frequencies of the molecule from spectroscopy. In the rotational formula, which for linear molecules is

$$s_r = R + R \ln (8\pi I k T / \sigma h^3) \qquad (5.11)$$

the effect is clear of an increase in the moment of inertia (I), which reduces the spacing of the rotational levels. The formula also shows a symmetry number σ, which is 1 for heteronuclear and 2 for homonuclear diatomic molecules (since they take up indistinguishable positions twice in a rotation). This symmetry number in the rotational entropy shows the systematic way of incorporating the type of consideration leading to the factor 4 in the equilibrium constant of the oxygen isotope reaction (4.1): $^{16}O_2$ and $^{18}O_2$ have $\sigma = 2$ and $^{16}O^{18}O$ has $\sigma = 1$. On this

73

account the symmetrical molecules have $R \ln 2$, i.e. 1·4 e.u., lower entropy than the unsymmetrical. At 25°C s_r may contribute about 30% of $s°_{298}$ for a gas.

The spacing of vibrational energy levels is simply hv and so increases directly with the frequency v, while the corresponding entropy contribution diminishes. At 25°C s_{vib} is usually much less than 5% of $s°_{298}$, but qualitative notions about the effects of distortions of vibrational potential energy curves on the entropies of the transition states of chemical reactions may still be informative even in condensed phases. Steepening the sides of a potential well decreases the entropy and making the well shallower increases it. (See, for example, C. K. Ingold, *Quart. Rev.*, 1957, 11, 1: especially pp. 9–12.)

§ 5.8 Free energy and the universal increase of entropy

If the total energy of a system is fixed changes take place towards the condition with the greatest number of quantum states ($\mathscr{P}$), i.e. with the greatest entropy. (See sections 4.1, 4.2 and 5.1.) The object now is to show that this simple criterion of increasing entropy justifies the form of the free energy, which determines the direction of chemical change at constant temperature and pressure.

Now a flask containing chemical reactants can exchange energy with its surroundings and so is not generally a system of constant energy. But it is always possible to include enough of the surroundings to make a new system such that all the energy exchanges are included within it. The system so defined (flask plus surroundings) then does not gain or lose energy but merely undergoes changes which redistribute its energy internally. It is now a system of constant energy and changes can only take place in such a way as to increase its overall entropy. Put in a different way, there are sets of energy levels characteristic both of the surroundings and of the contents of the flask; and the entire system, left to itself, merely shuffles the energy indiscriminately among the molecules in these levels inside and outside the flask until it arrives finally at the state of highest probability.

The condition for a spontaneous change is therefore $\Delta S > 0$, where ΔS represents the total overall increase in entropy. For those interested in the chemical reaction in the flask, however, it is useful to break this total entropy change down into an internal part, ΔS_i, corresponding to the change within the flask, and an external part, ΔS_e, corresponding to the change in the surroundings. The condition for a spontaneous change can then be written

$$\Delta S = \Delta S_e + \Delta S_i > 0 \qquad (5.12)$$

Of these two terms, ΔS_i is directly understood as the entropy change characteristic of the reaction in the flask. This entropy change, depending as it does only on the initial and final states, is the same whether the change is carried out reversibly or proceeds uncontrolled as in a natural process. The crucial step in the argument now is to realize that the entropy change in the surroundings, ΔS_e, can also be expressed *exactly* in terms of a quantity characteristic of the reaction occurring in the flask.

To see this, observe that the contents of the flask and the surroundings are on an essentially different footing with regard to the entropy changes that can take place, for the surroundings are supposed to be at equilibrium already and to act in a simple way, as a source or sink of heat, while attention is focused on the flask precisely because its contents may not be at equilibrium. When changes at constant temperature and pressure are considered, the surroundings have to be large enough for the heat exchange not to affect the temperature, and any expansion (or contraction) of the flask contents not to affect the pressure. In these circumstances the energy levels of the surroundings remain unchanged, and any increment of energy that may be received as heat from the flask contents is simply distributed among the molecules in those levels in the way characteristic of the temperature, just as if the heat were transferred reversibly from the chemical reaction mixture to the surroundings. Notice that even if there were temporary local heating in the immediate vicinity of the flask, by the time this became dissipated the final state of the surroundings would be the same as if the energy had been distributed evenly immediately; and the actual change in the external entropy, being only dependent on the initial and final states outside, would be the same, i.e. the heat received from the flask divided by the absolute temperature.

But the heat received from the flask by the surroundings at constant temperature and pressure is precisely the enthalpy loss of the contents of the flask, and so can be represented as $-\Delta H_i$, where ΔH_i stands for the enthalpy change characteristic of the reaction of interest within the flask. With this understanding therefore, ΔS_e can be identified with $-\Delta H_i/T$, and (5.12) can consequently be transformed into a relationship involving only quantities characteristic of the chemical reaction:

$$\Delta S = -\Delta H_i/T + \Delta S_i > 0 \qquad (5.13)$$

or, multiplying throughout by $-T$,

$$\Delta H_i - T\Delta S_i < 0 \qquad (5.14)$$

for a natural process.

It only remains to observe that both H and S are determined solely by the state of the system, so that a combination of them such as occurs in (5.14) is also a state function, and for isothermal processes at constant pressure the function, G, defined as $H - TS$, will evidently determine the direction of natural changes. It will also determine the position of equilibrium, when there is no tendency to change at all and ΔS, and hence $\Delta H_i - T\Delta S_i$, is zero.

The essential basis of this argument is that the entropy changes both in the chemical system and in the surroundings have to be taken into account in deciding whether or not a reaction can proceed spontaneously, and the entropy change in the surroundings is determined by the heat change characteristic of the reaction inside the flask. If the reaction were to take place at constant volume instead of constant pressure the appropriate measure of the heat absorbed by the surroundings would be $-\Delta U$, and the characteristic function determining the direction of change would be $U - TS$, i.e. A, instead of $H - TS$. In both cases the change in the appropriate function, A or G, measures the tendency for the change to take place and so gives the value for the work available when the natural process is harnessed. The difference between ΔH and ΔU is, of course, due to the unavailable work necessarily done against the constant pressure of the atmosphere if an expansion takes place. When other kinds of unavailable work become important the heat absorbed by the surroundings is related to ΔU in different ways from the ordinary ΔH, and a slightly different free-energy function therefore determines the direction of spontaneous change. For example, in the study of surface phases the work done against interfacial tension is important, and instead of $U + PV - TS$ a function incorporating the interfacial tension, γ, and the area, A', viz. $U + PV - \gamma A' - TS$, has to be used.

Under *reversible conditions* the reaction proceeds spontaneously in neither direction, because the internal entropy change ΔS_i is exactly balanced by the external change ΔS_e, and the overall ΔS, associated with the change in either direction, is therefore zero:

$$\Delta S = \Delta S_e + \Delta S_i = 0 \qquad (5.15)$$

The heat absorbed by the flask contents is then Q, and by the same argument as before ΔS_e is given in this case by $-Q/T$; whence ΔS_i is $+Q/T$, by (5.15). This justifies the statement that an entropy change can always be measured by the heat absorbed under reversible conditions divided by the temperature, whether there is an accompanying change in the energy (in the flask) or not.

Further work

Read Caldin, *Chemical Thermodynamics* (O.U.P., 1958), pp. 195–214, and examine Table 21 on p. 210.

Some useful qualitative ideas about the magnitude of standard entropies are discussed by R. T. Sanderson, *J. Chem. Educ.*, 1964, **41**, 13.

Other accounts covering various aspects of the material of this chapter will be found in:

Lewis and Randall, *Thermodynamics* (2nd edition, by Pitzer and Brewer, McGraw-Hill, 1961), Chapters 11 and 12.

Butler, *Chemical Thermodynamics* (4th edition, Macmillan, 1946), Chapter 13.

Introductory books on statistical mechanics are:

Guggenheim, *Boltzmann's Distribution Law* (North-Holland, Amsterdam, 1963): a little book with short chapters.

Rushbrooke, *Introduction to Statistical Mechanics* (O.U.P., 1949).

Hill, *Introduction to Statistical Thermodynamics* (Addison-Wesley, 1960.

Problems for Chapter 5

The books referred to are:

(P and B): Lewis and Randall, *Thermodynamics* (2nd edition, by Pitzer and Brewer, McGraw-Hill, 1961).

(L): Latimer's *Oxidation Potentials* (2nd edition, Prentice-Hall, 1952).

1. The standard entropies at 25°C of helium, neon, argon, krypton, xenon and radon are 30·13, 34·95, 36·98, 39·19, 40·53

and 42·10 e.u. Show that they agree with the mass dependence required by equation (5.9).

2. From (P and B), p. 680 (Table A7 — 7), calculate $s°_{298}$ for H_2 (g) and N_2 (g) and check your results with (L) or any other compilation you may find.

3. Use the same table (P and B) to evaluate $\Delta G°$ and K_p for the reaction

$$I_2 \text{ (g)} = 2I \text{ (g)}$$

at 1,000°K and 2,000°K.

4. Write down an expression for the entropy increase on expanding a mole of a perfect gas from volume v_1 to v_2. (See (4.8) and (5.9).)

5. Note that Δs for the vaporization of HCl is about 21 e.u. Find data for l_v and the boiling-point of C_6H_6 and ether, calculate their entropies of vaporization and comment on the results. (Demonstration of Trouton's rule.) See Timmermans, *Physicochemical Constants of Organic Compounds* (Elsevier, 1950) for data.

6. Ignoring rotational effects, try out the (very) rough rule that the production of each mole of a gas contributes about 21 e.u. to the entropy on the following reaction:

$$N_2 \text{ (g)} + 3H_2 \text{ (g)} = 2NH_3 \text{ (g)}$$

Estimate the entropy of the reaction first by the rough rule and then calculate the actual value from tables in (L) or elsewhere.

Comment on the rough magnitudes and directions of the rotational entropy effects in this case.

7. A ball is dropped from a height and finally comes to rest. Discuss the change between the initial and final states in terms of § 5.8. (This puts the remarks at the beginning of Chapter 4 into perspective.)

6

Some Useful Equations

The principal results of this chapter are the formulae for the variation of chemical potentials and ΔG with temperature. These are shown to arise, along with some other useful equations, from a systematic development of the relationships between the various thermodynamic properties.

§ 6.1 The degrees of freedom of a system

All the quantities U, H, G, V, S, P, T, etc., have fixed values for a given state of the system. There are many properties of this kind, and it is clear that they cannot all be varied independently: there is a minimum number of them required to fix the state of a system completely, and this is called the number of *degrees of freedom* of the system and represented by the symbol F.

Only two variables are needed to specify completely the state of a fixed quantity of a gas. If the pressure and temperature are fixed the volume is also fixed, for there is always an appropriate equation of state connecting these three variables, even if the perfect gas equation, $PV = nRT$, is not applicable. The specification of two out of the three variables (apart from n) in this equation is sufficient to fix not only the third but also all the other properties like U, H, G, S, etc. (There is no guarantee that these functions are *easily* calculable, just that they are physically fixed. The actual equations necessary for their calculation may be very complicated or not even precisely known.) If the number of moles of the gas (n) is also varied, clearly a third degree of freedom is introduced, since all the extensive properties are affected by the quantity of material. Furthermore, if the gas is a mixture of several (say c) component substances, all of which can be increased in amount, the number of degrees of freedom is increased to c + 2. Solids and liquids are also subject to equations of state linking P, V and T, so the formula

$$\text{F} = \text{c} + 2 \qquad\qquad (6.1)$$

gives *the number of degrees of freedom in any single-phase system which can be varied in quantity* (provided that no extra degrees of freedom due to the presence of variable gravitational, magnetic or electrical fields, etc., are brought into operation).

It is important to have a precise idea of what is meant by c, the *number of components*. c is not simply the number of chemical substances present, but the minimum number of these required to specify completely the composition of *every phase* present. For example, solid NH_4Cl in equilibrium with a vapour formed only of NH_3 and HCl in equimolar proportions is a 1-component system, but becomes a 2-component system if the NH_3 and HCl are disproportionated. On the other hand, solid $CaCO_3$ in equilibrium with CaO and CO_2 is always a 2-component system because the CaO (solid) and CO_2 (gas) occur in different phases, and CaO is needed to specify the one and CO_2 the other: the composition of $CaCO_3$ can of course be described in terms of these two. When inter-related chemical substances occur in this way, which set of c you choose as the components is a matter of convenience.

§ 6.2 An expression for a small change in the total energy of a system with variable n_i

Suppose first of all that a small change is brought about at constant temperature and pressure and also reversibly, so that the heat absorbed can be equated to $T\mathrm{d}S$ and the work done to dW or dW′ $+ P\mathrm{d}V$ (equation (1.6)). Suppose also that all the various components are increased by the amounts $\mathrm{d}n_i$ which are small enough not to affect the values of the μ_i. Then for each addition an amount of work $\mu_i \mathrm{d}n_i$ is done *on* the system (i.e. its chemical potential energy is increased by this amount) and the total of all these contributions to dW′ (done *by* the system) is therefore $-\sum_i \mu_i \mathrm{d}n_i$. Since d$U$ is dQ $-$ dW, then

$$\mathrm{d}U = T\mathrm{d}S - P\mathrm{d}V + \sum_i \mu_i \mathrm{d}n_i \qquad (6.2)$$

This important equation is clearly an adequate equation of state, since it expresses changes in U in terms of the c $+$ 2 variables S, V and $n_1, n_2, \ldots n_C$. Although it was derived for the very special case of a reversible change at constant T and P therefore, it must be generally applicable for any small change between two specified equilibrium states, whether the transition is made reversibly or not and whether T and P are held constant or not, since S, V and the n_i are sufficient to define the state (and hence U) completely. (The effects of any changes in T and P will, of course, be reflected in the actual values of dS and dV for the change.) Because of this, the variables (S, V, $n_1, n_2, \ldots n_C$) on the right-hand side of (6.2) can be varied one at a time, keeping all the others fixed (i.e. setting all but one of dS, dV, dn_1, dn_2, etc., equal to zero) to give the following exact equations for the partial differential coefficients:

$$(\partial U/\partial S)_{V,\, n_i} = T \qquad (\partial U/\partial V)_{S,\, n_i} = -P$$
$$(\partial U/\partial n_i)_{S,\, V,\, n_j} = \mu_i \qquad (6.3)$$

As before, the subscripts outside the brackets stand for the variables which are held constant during the differentiations represented by the curly d's; and n_j stands for all the composition variables except the one (n_i) being varied.

§ 6.3 The systematic method of Willard Gibbs

It is notoriously easy to make mistakes in deriving thermodynamic equations from first physical principles, and even those experienced in particular applications of thermodynamics often feel unconfident faced with a new type of problem and would feel much more so if they had always to begin in this way. It is therefore very useful to have at hand the easily constructed scaffolding of exact relations between the various thermodynamic functions provided by Gibbs. Beginning with equation (6.2), the method is to work from precise definitions of the functions H, A and G in terms of U, T, S, P and V, so that equivalent expressions to (6.2) can be obtained for dH, dA and dG. The usefulness of these functions can then be demonstrated afterwards by showing how they can be related to experimental heat and work quantities.

Thus:

Define $H = U + PV$. Then $dH = dU + PdV + VdP$, or by substituting dU from (6.2)

$$dH = TdS + VdP + \sum_i \mu_i dn_i \qquad (6.4)$$

Thus H can be expressed as a function of the $c + 2$ quantities S, P and the n_i; and by dealing with each variable on its own in turn

$$(\partial H/\partial S)_{P, n_i} = T \qquad (\partial H/\partial P)_{S, n_i} = V$$
$$(\partial H/\partial n_i)_{S, P, n_j} = \mu_i \qquad (6.5)$$

At constant pressure, $dH = dU + PdV = dq - dw + PdV$; and when the only work (dw) done in an experiment is PdV (pushing back the atmosphere) $dH = dq$, the heat absorbed, as we have noticed before.

The change in enthalpy is measured by the heat absorbed

at constant pressure when a process is not harnessed to do external work.

Define $A = U - TS$. Then $dA = dU - TdS - SdT$, or by (6.2)

$$dA = -SdT - PdV + \sum_i \mu_i dn_i \qquad (6.6)$$

$$(\partial A/\partial T)_{V, n_i} = -S \qquad (\partial A/\partial V)_{T, n_i} = -P$$
$$(\partial A/\partial n_i)_{T, V, n_j} = \mu_i \qquad (6.7)$$

At constant temperature, $dA = dU - TdS = dq - dw - TdS$. But if the change is carried out reversibly, so that $dw = dW$ and $dq = TdS$, the change in A is $dA = -dW$.

The decrease in the function A is measured by the maximum work done by the system at constant temperature, and if a change in a closed system is carried out in such a way that all this work is available for harnessing (i.e. at constant volume so that there is no PdV term) the function A gives a measure of the tendency for the change to take place. (By a 'closed' system is meant one in which no materials are gained or lost by the system as a whole, although substances may be transformed chemically or pass from one phase to another within the system.)

Define $G = U + PV - TS = H - TS$. Then
$$dG = dU + PdV + VdP - TdS - SdT$$
or $\qquad dG = dH - TdS - SdT.$
From either (6.2) or (6.4),

$$dG = -SdT + VdP + \sum_i \mu_i dn_i \qquad (6.8)$$

$$(\partial G/\partial T)_{P, n_i} = -S \qquad (\partial G/\partial P)_{T, n_i} = V$$
$$(\partial G/\partial n_i)_{T, P, n_j} = \mu_i \qquad (6.9)$$

For a small change at constant temperature and pressure, $dG = dq - dw + PdV - TdS$. If the change is carried out reversibly, so that $dq = TdS$, $dG = -(dW - PdV)$, i.e. $dG = -dW'$.

The decrease in the function G is measured by the maximum available work when the change is carried out at constant temperature and pressure, and for these conditions is therefore a measure of the tendency for a change to take place in a closed system.

Notice particularly that the functions G and A only correspond to work terms in restricted conditions: ΔG is not always a measure of the maximum work available from a process, only when the temperature and pressure are constant. There are even conditions in which ΔU and ΔH are equivalent to work terms and so measure the tendencies of changes to take place, and the easy way to see what these conditions are for any of the functions U, H, A or G is to see what must be done to eliminate the first two terms on the right-hand side of (6.2), (6.4), (6.6) or (6.8). (For example, ΔU measures the tendency for a change to take place in a closed system when the entropy and volume are held constant.) In all cases the directions of chemical change are determined by combinations of chemical potentials, just as would be expected from Chapter 1.

§ 6.4 Some more G equations

Integration of (6.8) at constant T and P gives

$$G = \sum_i \mu_i n_i \qquad (6.10)$$

if the integration constant is eliminated by setting the zeros of the G and μ_i scales consistently. Any relationship between quantities characterized by the state of the system at equilibrium is independent of the way the state is arrived at; so G is always given by the sum of the $\mu_i n_i$, and any small change in G between well-defined equilibrium states must be given by the sum of $d(\mu_i n_i)$: i.e.

$$dG = \sum_i n_i d\mu_i + \sum_i \mu_i dn_i \qquad (6.11)$$

G

Since both (6.8) and (6.11) are general expressions for dG, it follows that

$$\sum_i n_i \mathrm{d}\mu_i = -S\mathrm{d}T + V\mathrm{d}P \tag{6.12}$$

For changes at constant temperature and pressure (dT and dP both zero) the μ_i can evidently not be varied independently: there is always a relationship between the dμ_i,

$$\sum_i n_i \mathrm{d}\mu_i = 0 \tag{6.13}$$

This is usually known as *the Gibbs–Duhem equation* and is used in binary systems for obtaining changes in the chemical potential of one component from equilibrium measurements on the other.

For shifts in equilibria with temperature it is easier to deal with G/T rather than G itself. ($\Delta G/T = 0$ is just as good a criterion of equilibrium at constant T and P as $\Delta G = 0$.)

By differentiation

$$\left(\frac{\partial(G/T)}{\partial T}\right)_P = \frac{1}{T}\left(\frac{\partial G}{\partial T}\right)_P - \frac{G}{T^2} = -\frac{S}{T} - \frac{G}{T^2}$$

$$= -\frac{1}{T^2}(TS + G) = -\frac{H}{T^2} \tag{6.14}$$

In this derivation, the first equation of (6.9) and the definition of G as $H - TS$ have been used.

The next important step is to see that (6.14) and the first two equations of (6.9), all of which relate extensive properties on the two sides of the equation, apply equally well to the Δ values of these quantities corresponding to chemical change as to the quantities themselves, because each of the equations can be applied both to the products and to the reactants:

$$\left(\frac{\partial \Delta G}{\partial T}\right)_P = \left(\frac{\partial[G_{\text{products}} - G_{\text{reactants}}]}{\partial T}\right)_P$$

$$= \left(\frac{\partial G_{\text{prod.}}}{\partial T}\right)_P - \left(\frac{\partial G_{\text{react.}}}{\partial T}\right)_P$$

$$= -[S_{\text{prod.}} - S_{\text{react.}}] = -\Delta S \tag{6.15}$$

Similarly,

$$\left(\frac{\partial \Delta G}{\partial P}\right)_P = \Delta V \qquad (6.16)$$

$$\left(\frac{\partial(\Delta G/T)}{\partial T}\right)_P = -\frac{\Delta H}{T^2} \qquad (6.17)$$

In terms of the products and reactants in their standard states,

$$\left(\frac{\partial(\Delta G^\ominus/T)}{\partial T}\right)_P = -\frac{\Delta H^\ominus}{T^2} \qquad (6.18)$$

§ 6.5 The variation of equilibrium constants with temperature

Application of (6.18) to the reaction isotherm (2.17) leads immediately to the very important equation

$$\left(\frac{\partial \ln K}{\partial T}\right)_P = \frac{\Delta H^\ominus}{RT^2} \qquad (6.19)$$

(This equation is often known as *the reaction isochore*, though that name should strictly refer to constant volume, not constant pressure conditions.) From (2.14) a special form of (6.19) is obtained with K_p and ΔH°.

The reaction isochore expresses quantitatively the idea involved when le Chatelier's principle is applied to equilibrium shifts with temperature: if $\Delta H^\ominus$ is positive, i.e. heat is absorbed in the reaction, K goes up as the temperature is raised and more of the products are formed at equilibrium, while a negative $\Delta H^\ominus$ has the opposite effect.

Over a moderate temperature range, (6.19) can often be integrated with sufficient accuracy on the assumption that $\Delta H^\ominus$ is constant:

$$\ln\left(\frac{K_2}{K_1}\right) = -\frac{\Delta H^\ominus}{R}\left(\frac{1}{T_2} - \frac{1}{T_1}\right) \qquad (6.20)$$

If K_1 is the known value of K at the temperature $T_1(^\circ K)$ the value K_2 at some other temperature T_2 can therefore be obtained if $\Delta H^\ominus$ is known.

The principles for further refinements allowing for the temperature variation of $\Delta H^\ominus$ have already been dealt with in Chapter 3: $\partial \Delta H^\ominus / \partial T = \Delta C^\ominus_p$. The next approximation would be to take $\Delta C^\ominus_p$ as constant and substitute the resulting temperature-dependent $\Delta H^\ominus$ in (6.19) before integrating; and the most precise equation of all is obtained by allowing for the temperature dependence of $\Delta C^\ominus_p$. There is just one thing to be careful of in these integrations: $\Delta C^\ominus_p$ has to be expressed explicitly as a function of temperature (such as a power series) *before* the integration to give $\Delta H^\ominus$ as a function of temperature, and this function has to be substituted in (6.19) *before* integration (*not* in (6.20)) to give the correct integrated form for ln K. In this way the original power series for $\Delta C^\ominus_p$ undergoes two integrations.

Although it is worth knowing just how the isochore can be integrated exactly, much of the actual labour of calculation can be avoided by using tables of the function $-(g^\circ - h^\circ_{T'})/T$ when available for all the substances occurring in a chemical reaction. At any listed temperature the Δ value of this function is worked out in the familiar way:

$$\Delta[-(G^\circ - H^\circ_{T'})/T] = \sum \nu[-(g^\circ - h^\circ_{T'})/T]_{\text{products}}$$
$$- \sum \nu[-(g^\circ - h^\circ_{T'})/T]_{\text{reactants}} \quad (6.21)$$

The $h^\circ_{T'}$ values are also provided so that ΔH° at the standard temperature T' (either 298° or 0°K) can be obtained, divided by T, and then subtracted from the result of (6.21) to give $\Delta G^\circ_T/T$ and hence K at the required temperature. If K is required at temperatures intermediate between those actually listed you are recommended to interpolate after calculating the difference (6.21) for neighbouring temperatures, as such differences vary less with temperature than the listed values themselves.

§ 6.6 ΔS and ΔH from e.m.f. measurements

By combining $G = H - TS$ with $S = -\partial G/\partial T$ from (6.9)

$$G = H + T(\partial G/\partial T) \qquad (6.22)$$

The corresponding difference equation is

$$\Delta G = \Delta H + T(\partial \Delta G/\partial T) \qquad (6.23)$$

In e.m.f. experiments ΔG for the cell reaction is measured as $-nFE$ (equation (1.9)).

Hence $\qquad \Delta H = -nFE + nFT(\partial E/\partial T) \qquad (6.24)$

Also $\qquad \Delta S = nF(\partial E/\partial T) \qquad (6.25)$

The increase of the e.m.f. with temperature is therefore a direct measure of the entropy change of the cell reaction, and when multiplied by nFT is equal to the heat absorbed during the reversible working of the cell. The latter added to ΔG (equation (6.24)) gives ΔH from e.m.f. measurements alone. (Notice that the heat absorbed when the reaction is unharnessed, ΔH, is equal to the work done *on* the system, ΔG, plus the heat absorbed, $T\Delta S$, when the same reaction is carried out reversibly.)

§ 6.7 Partial molar quantities

The equations (6.15), (6.16) and (6.17) can be applied not only to chemical reactions but also to other cases of specified initial and final states.

Suppose a mole of a substance is added to a very large quantity of a solution under conditions of constant temperature and pressure. Then equations (6.9) and (6.14) apply both to the state before the addition and to that after it, and (6.15), (6.16) and (6.17) then relate to the corresponding ΔG, ΔS, ΔV and ΔH, the Δ in each case signifying the final minus the initial value of each extensive variable. All these quantities then represent the changes in the various extensive properties of the system on adding a mole of the substance in question to a very large amount of the solution, keeping the temperature, pressure and the amounts of all the other components fixed, and they are known as *partial molar quantities*.

A much smaller amount of the substance can, of course, be added and the effects adjusted to increments per mole, by division by the fraction of a mole, dn_i, added. The partial molar quantities can therefore be formulated as follows:

$$g_i = (\partial G/\partial n_i)_{T, P, n_j} \qquad s_i = (\partial S/\partial n_i)_{T, P, n_j}$$
$$v_i = (\partial V/\partial n_i)_{T, P, n_j} \qquad h_i = (\partial H/\partial n_i)_{T, P, n_j} \quad (6.26)$$

and the relations between them corresponding to (6.15), (6.16) and (6.17) are therefore

$$\partial\mu_i/\partial T = -s_i \qquad\qquad (6.27)$$
$$\partial\mu_i/\partial P = v_i \qquad\qquad (6.28)$$
$$\partial(\mu_i/T)/\partial T = -h_i/T^2 \qquad\qquad (6.29)$$

because comparison of the first equation of (6.26) with the last of (6.9) shows that *the partial molar Gibbs free energy is identical with the chemical potential*. (The chemical potential is, however, of wider application than G quantities, as the last sentence in § 6.3 indicates.)

Where there is more than one component in a phase, partial molar quantities will always crop up whenever the variations of chemical potentials with temperature and pressure are required. In such systems they are also the correct molar quantities to be used in expressions for the overall change in any extensive property accompanying a chemical reaction:

$$\Delta H = (\sum_i \nu_i h_i)_{\text{products}} - (\sum_i \nu_i h_i)_{\text{reactants}} \qquad (6.30)$$
$$\Delta V = (\sum_i \nu_i v_i)_{\text{products}} - (\sum_i \nu_i v_i)_{\text{reactants}} \qquad (6.31)$$
$$\Delta C_p = (\sum_i \nu_i c_{pi})_{\text{products}} - (\sum_i \nu_i c_{pi})_{\text{reactants}} \qquad (6.32)$$

For example, the overall volume change when a reaction takes place to a small extent is simply the volume increase caused by the small additions of the products, in their correct stoichiometric proportions, to the solution as it stands, less the corresponding amounts for the reactants which are disappearing from the solution. 'Small' additions (or additions to a large quantity of solution) are specified because these partial molar quantities are often rather sensitive to composition and could therefore alter significantly even over the composition range covered by only a moderate addition. (Look once again at § 1.3.)

Because of the dilution effect, μ_i and s_i are both essentially concentration-dependent; both h_i and v_i in solutions also differ more from the molar quantities of the pure substances than you might at first suppose, due to variations in extents of chemical reactions, inter-molecular forces, and shapes and sizes for packing. For example, adding very small molecules to a liquid composed of very large ones might cause practically no volume change because of the spaces that can be filled up.

§ 6.8 The measurement of partial molar quantities

Some of the most precise determinations of h_i are made directly by adding small quantities of one component to a large quantity of solution in a calorimeter and measuring the temperature rise. (See, for example, the work of J. E. Kunzler and W. F. Giauque on the water–sulphuric acid system, *J. Amer. Chem. Soc.*, 1952, **74**, 3472.) Even a small addition causes a significant change in composition, and the procedure is to assign the experimentally determined quantity $\Delta H/\Delta n_i$ to the composition corresponding to a point half-way through the addition, $n_i + \Delta n_i/2$, and this allows very well for slight differences in h_i before and after the addition. The aim is to make the additions small enough to follow fluctuations in h_i faithfully, without surrendering experimental precision.

When accurate density data are available at sufficiently

closely spaced concentrations they can be recast as follows to calculate v_i in the same direct way.

For binary mixtures of the substances A and B (with molecular weights M_A and M_B), suppose that at the weight fraction w of B the solution density is ρ. (The weight fraction is the wt % divided by 100.) The volume of 1 g of this solution is $1/\rho$ and the volume which contains 1 g of B, and $(1 - w)/wg$ of A, is $1/\rho w$. At a neighbouring weight fraction w', where the density is ρ', the volume which contains 1 g of B, and $(1 - w')/w'$ of A, is $1/\rho'w'$.

Thus, the total volume of a solution containing the fixed 1 g of B would increase by $1/\rho'w' - 1/\rho w$ on adding the small quantity $(1 - w')/w' - (1 - w)/w$ g of A only. The volume increase per mole is therefore

$$v_A = M_A \left[\frac{1}{\rho'w'} - \frac{1}{\rho w} \right] \Big/ \left[\frac{(1 - w')}{w'} - \frac{(1 - w)}{w} \right] \quad (6.33)$$

To maintain accuracy in computation without resorting to many-figured tables, it is best to work on differences where possible and to use (6.33) in the form

$$v_A = \frac{M_A}{\rho\rho'} \left[\rho - \frac{(\rho - \rho')w'}{(w' - w)} \right] \quad (6.34)$$

For example, if A is ethanol and B water, tables of densities at 15 °C show that at 19% ethanol ($w = 0.81$) ρ is 0.97191 g cm^{-3} and at 20% ethanol ($w' = 0.80$) ρ' is 0.97069 g cm^{-3}. Therefore at 19·5% ethanol

$$v_{C_2H_5OH} = \frac{46.068 \text{ cm}^3}{0.97191 \times 0.97069} \left[0.97191 - \frac{(0.00122) \times 0.80}{(-0.01)} \right]$$

$$= \underline{52.2 \text{ cm}^3}$$

(This is almost 6 cm^3 lower than $v°_{C_2H_5OH}$, the molar volume of pure ethanol, which is 46.068/0.79354 or $\underline{58.1 \text{ cm}^3}$)

§ 6.9 The interrelation of partial molar quantities

By interchanging A and B in this last example, clearly the same data can be used to calculate both v_A and v_B. Evidently the v_i, like the μ_i, cannot be varied independently (cf. equation (6.13)).

At a fixed temperature and pressure each infinitesimal addition of dn_i moles of each substance increases the volume of a system by $v_i dn_i$. The effect on the total volume of the addition of several components is therefore

$$dV = v_1 dn_1 + v_2 dn_2 + \ldots \qquad (6.35)$$

But since partial molar quantities depend only on the ratios of the n_i and not on the total amount of solution, this equation can be integrated up from zero volume easily by keeping the dn_i increments in the same ratios so that the v_i cannot vary:

$$V = \sum_i v_i n_i \text{ (cf. 6.10)} \qquad (6.36)$$

In any small change between two states (not necessarily keeping the n_i in the same ratios), all the changes in the v_i must therefore be related, since (6.36) applies to both states, and this can only be the case if

$$dV = \sum_i v_i dn_i + \sum_i n_i dv_i \qquad (6.37)$$

For both (6.35) and (6.37) to hold simultaneously

$$\sum_i n_i dv_i = 0 \qquad (6.38)$$

An equation like this applies to all partial molar quantities and is sometimes used in binary solutions for obtaining changes in partial quantities for one component from data relating to the other. The most important equation of this kind is (6.13), which gives solute activities from equilibrium measurements on the solvent.

§ 6.10 Final remarks on partial molar quantities

Many people are puzzled at first by partial molar quantities, which they find difficult to visualize compared with the straightforward molar properties of a pure substance. Nevertheless, the physical idea behind partial molar quantities arises quite naturally whenever a change is considered.

Suppose, for example, that you want to know if a chemical system is at equilibrium. Clearly if any change is to occur at all it must start off as a small change, and a small change can only occur spontaneously (at constant temperature and pressure) if G can decrease. Now directly any chemical change begins to occur, minute quantities of the reactants disappear and minute quantities of the products are produced in exactly the ratios specified in the corresponding chemical equation; and the total change in any of the extensive properties, H, G, V, etc., is then seen to be calculable only from combinations of the partial molar quantities *appropriate to the mixture as it stands*. The system has no way of knowing what the molar volumes, free energies, etc., may be in the pure state if this is not actually present: it is only concerned with the changes that occur when a minute quantity of each component vanishes or makes its appearance in a particular mixture, and this is exactly what partial molar quantities are designed to measure. Thus, the ΔG of the process just described (multiplied up to molar amounts) is given by the sum of the $\nu_i \mu_i$ (i.e. $\nu_i g_i$) terms for the products less that for the reactants, while the corresponding ΔH and ΔV for exactly the same process are given by the same formula with h_i and v_i in place of μ_i, the h_i, v_i and μ_i all being partial molar quantities.

It is also important to grasp clearly that when ΔG and ΔS, ΔV or ΔH appear on opposite sides of equations like (6.15), (6.16) and (6.17) they must refer to exactly the same process. Imagine, for example, solid sodium hydroxide in equilibrium with its saturated aqueous solution at a certain temperature.

Equilibrium exists because the transference of a mole of sodium and hydroxide ions from the crystal lattice to (a large quantity of) the liquid is accompanied by no change in the free energy: $\Delta G = 0$, or alternatively, $\Delta G/T = 0$. If the temperature is increased slightly, whether $\Delta G/T$ for this process becomes negative or positive depends upon the sign of ΔH, by (6.17), i.e. upon whether heat is absorbed or evolved when sodium hydroxide is dissolved *in the saturated solution*. If $\Delta G/T$ becomes negative (and more caustic soda dissolves) this is because ΔH is positive, i.e. the quantity $h_{Na^+} + h_{OH^-}$ is greater in the liquid than in the solid phase; but only the partial molar enthalpies in the solid and the *saturated* solution are relevant. As a matter of fact, the hydroxide ion (like the hydrogen ion) is so heavily hydrated in dilute aqueous solution that the sum $h_{Na^+} + h_{OH^-}$ is considerably less in the liquid than in the solid phase and, as is very well known, a large amount of heat is evolved on dissolving the solid in water. But as the solution becomes more concentrated, less water becomes available for hydration until a point is reached at which there is insufficient for the full hydration of the OH^- ion and $h_{Na^+} + h_{OH^-}$ rises steeply and, in very concentrated solutions, exceeds the value for the solid. According to this line of argument, rather insoluble hydroxides would generally be expected to decrease in solubility with increasing temperature and extremely soluble ones to increase.

When pure substances are involved the changes in the extensive properties on adding or taking away a mole are, of course, fixed, at a fixed temperature and pressure: the partial molar quantities are simply the ordinary quantities per mole. But when we are interested in equilibrium or the tendency to change it is best to think first in terms of partial molar quantities for all the phases concerned and to welcome the simplification produced by constant values of these quantities when they crop up. For this reason, the small letter symbols, h_i, v_i, etc., always stand for partial molar quantities in this book. If a pure substance is taken as a standard state the symbols $h°_i$, $v°_i$, etc., then automatically refer to the ordinary molar quantities as special cases.

After Chapters 5 and 6 a fuller appreciation of the significance of the chemical potential is possible. Consider, for example, an aqueous solution with water vapour over it. On transferring a mole of water isothermally from (a large quantity of) the liquid (superscript l) to the vapour (superscript g, for gas), there is an enthalpy increase of $^gh - {}^lh$ and an entropy increase of $^gs - {}^ls$, all the partial molar quantities referring to the species H_2O. The overall entropy increase (including the surroundings) when the transfer occurs freely is $-(^gh - {}^lh)/T + (^gs - {}^ls)$, as in § 5.8, and H_2O molecules will pass spontaneously into the vapour phase if this overall ΔS is positive,

i.e. if $$(^gh - {}^lh)/T < (^gs - {}^ls)$$

or $$(^gh - T^gs) < (^lh - T^ls) \qquad (6.39)$$

This quantity, which has to be greater in the liquid for vaporization to occur, is the same as g, or μ.

The tendency to change is here understood in terms of the redistribution of energy and molecules until the state of highest probability is reached, and this removes the necessity for thinking of special contrivances (which often look highly artificial) for harnessing natural changes. Nevertheless, if the tendency to change *can* be opposed successfully and then allowed to operate in a controlled manner there is nothing unreal about the work available, which would be $(^g\mu - {}^l\mu)$ in the above example.

Further work

Inspect the original source of the Gibbs method (*The Collected Works of J. Willard Gibbs*, Yale U.P., 1928, pp. 85–92) and notice the different way of introducing the chemical potentials (p. 63) and setting up equation (6.2) from that given here.

Modern accounts of this method are: E. A. Guggenheim, *Thermodynamics* (North Holland, 2nd edition, 1950, pp. 17–22); and E. F. Caldin, *Chemical Thermodynamics* (O.U.P., 1958, pp. 162–167).

For further information on the determination of partial molar quantities see Lewis and Randall (*Thermodynamics*, 2nd edition, by Pitzer and Brewer), pp. 205–213. (Notice, however, that, despite their elegance, methods which depend on drawing tangents to curves are generally not very precise.)

Sections on the integration of the isochore can also be read at this stage: e.g. Caldin, op. cit., pp. 241–250.

Problems for Chapter 6

1. From the Landolt–Börnstein Tables, supplement IIIa (Eg IIIa), p. 396 (or from any other tables), find the densities of ethanol–water mixtures at $15°C$ at 1, 2, 99 and 100% ethanol and estimate, using (6.34), the partial molar volumes of both ethanol and water at $1·5\%$ and $99·5\%$ ethanol.

2. $\Delta g°_{298} = 20·719$ kcal mole^{-1} and $\Delta h°_{298} = 21·600$ kcal mole^{-1} for the formation of NO (g). Estimate the approximate temperature at which an equimolar mixture of nitrogen and oxygen contains equal quantities of N_2, O_2 and NO molecules. (Use equation (6.20) or an equivalent form.)

3. Produce integrated forms of the isochore (6.19), beginning $R\ln K = \ldots$, based on each of the following empirical equations for the temperature variation of ΔC_p.

(a) $\Delta C_p = a + bT + cT^{-2}$

(b) $\Delta C_p = a' + b'T + c'T^2$

(Remember the integration constant at each stage.)

4. For the reaction

$$CaCO_3 \text{ (s)} = CaO \text{ (s)} + CO_2 \text{ (g)}$$

$\Delta G°$ at any temperature is given by the difference between the standard free energies of formation of CaO (s) and CO_2 (g) less that of $CaCO_3$ (s), but the equilibrium constant is simply p_{CO_2} since the solids remain in their standard states and at the same chemical potential in any isothermal transformation.

Use the (P and B) tables, pp. 676 and 682, to calculate accurately the equilibrium pressure of CO_2 over $CaCO_3$ and CaO at 550°C. Can $CaCO_3$ be kept unchanged at this temperature in the ordinary atmosphere?

(The function for CO_2 has to be converted to $-(g° - h°_{298})/T$ first by adding $(h°_{298} - h°_0)/T$. The values of $-(\Delta G° - \Delta H°_{298})/T$ for the reaction can then be calculated at 500°K and 1,000°K and that for 550°C interpolated. To get $-(\Delta G°/T)$ at 550°C, the enthalpies of formation at 298°K must be used to give the enthalpy change for the whole reaction at 298° before division by T and subtraction.)

Compare the result with that obtained from equation (6.20) using $\Delta G°_{298}$ and $\Delta H°_{298}$ only (from (L) or other tables).

7

Chemical Potentials in Solution

§ 7.1 Activity

In Chapter 2 the activity was introduced to play the same role in solutions as the partial pressure does in gases, and thus to maintain the simple form of the equilibrium formulae. Since at equilibrium the chemical potential of a species has to be the same in solution and in the vapour, the equations

$$^g\mu_i = {}^g\mu^\circ_i + RT \ln p_i \qquad (2.9)$$

and
$$^l\mu_i = {}^l\mu^\ominus_i + RT \ln a_i \qquad (2.15)$$

mean that the activity of a species is proportional to its vapour pressure. (The upper prefixes g and l stand for gas and liquid.) The proportionality constant between a_i and p_i is fixed at a given temperature by fixing the standard state in the liquid, at which $^l\mu_i = {}^l\mu^\ominus_i$ and $a_i = 1$. If the vapour pressure over this standard state is $p^\ominus_i$ the activity of the species in some other solution over which its vapour pressure is p_i must be

$$a_i = p_i/p^\ominus_i \qquad (7.1)$$

On the *rational scale*, $p^\ominus_i$ is p°_i, the vapour pressure of the pure substance i in the liquid state at the required temperature and $^l\mu^\ominus_i$ can be written as $^l\mu^\circ_i$. (For solid solutions, p°_i refers to the pure solid.)

The activity of a volatile substance can therefore be directly determined by vapour-pressure measurements. If more than one constituent of a solution is volatile the partial pressure of each constituent has to be determined by measuring both the total vapour pressure and the vapour-phase composition (by analysing a condensed sample). The total pressure can then be divided up (if there are no vapour-phase reactions) into partial pressures in proportion to the numbers of moles of each substance present in the vapour phase; or if y_i is the mole fraction of the substance i in the vapour phase, i.e. $y_i = n_i/(n_1 + n_2 + . . .)$, and P is the total vapour pressure,

$$p_i = y_i P \qquad (7.2)$$

Division by the vapour pressure of the pure substance at the same temperature then yields the rational activity a_i.

Vapour pressures are commonly used for activity determinations both for mixtures of organic liquids and for solutions of electrolytes in volatile solvents. Strangely enough, although the principal method for determining the activity of water in moderately concentrated electrolytic solutions is a vapour-pressure method, it requires no pressure measurements at all once the reference scale has been established by accurate measurements on a range of concentrations for a single reference solute, such as potassium chloride. Accurately weighed samples of known concentrations of the reference substance and the substance under investigation are kept in separate platinum dishes in the same vacuum desiccator, which is rocked gently in a thermostat. Water distils from one solution to the other until they both have the same vapour pressure, or are *isopiestic*. Since water is the only volatile constituent, the compositions of the final solutions are simply determined by reweighing to find the correction for the loss or gain in weight. The known vapour pressure of the final solution of potassium chloride is then also the vapour pressure of the final solution of the other substance.

This *isopiestic method* is the principal source of activity data for electrolyte solutions at concentrations above 0·1 molal. It does, of course, rest completely on the very accurate direct measurements made on the reference solutions.

To get the solute activity from the solvent vapour pressures the Gibbs–Duhem equation (6.13) is used in the form

$$\int d \ln a_2 = -\int (n_1/n_2) d \ln a_1 \qquad (7.3)$$

by measuring the area under a graph of (n_1/n_2) against $\ln p_1$ or some procedure equivalent to this; and the integration constant is determined by the choice of standard state for the solute. Since only changes in the logarithms of the activities are related in (7.3), any multiple of a scale of activities will satisfy the Gibbs–Duhem equation equally well, and a different convention can therefore be used for the standard state of a solute from that of the solvent, which is always on a rational scale.

Some other methods of determining activities will be mentioned later.

§ 7.2 The perfect solution

When the activity was introduced in Chapter 2 some idea of its meaning was acquired by recognizing that concentration is a good approximation to activity for certain types of dilute solution. To go farther than this a more detailed study of the nature of solutions is helpful.

To serve as a reference for the properties of all solutions, a *perfect solution* is devised, analogous to the perfect gas. Unfortunately for the beginner, however, deviations from this norm are much more important than is the case with gases at ordinary pressures; and this is indeed to be expected, since the molecules in a gas only have to be far enough apart most of the time for their interactions to be unimportant, whereas in solution they are necessarily close together, and variations in their interaction energies could therefore be very significant.

To understand the equilibrium properties of a solution formed by mixing two liquids together, you have to consider both the energy and the entropy changes involved. The energy change in forming a perfect solution (from the pure liquids) is specified quite simply: it is zero. If one pure liquid is composed of A molecules and the other of B molecules this means that the energy required to take either an A or a B molecule from its surroundings in the pure liquid must be recovered exactly when the molecule is transferred to the solution. In other words, the partial molar energy of a component of a perfect solution is the same as its molar energy in the pure liquid. This occurs when the A–A, A–B and B–B interactions are all very similar and the molecules in all three situations have the same number of near neighbours.

The entropy changes are characterized by specifying that the molecules must be of similar size so that they can replace one another indiscriminately without distortion of the three-dimensional pattern they form in space. It makes the counting easier to think of this pattern as a lattice like the crystal lattices formed by molecules in solids, but the results obtained do not really require such a rigid structure: it is the ability to replace one molecule by another without much distortion that is important. An increase in entropy arises on mixing the components simply because the molecules of both types have more 'lattice' sites available to them for distribution after they are mixed. If the tendency for the pure components to diffuse into one another to form a perfect solution is made to do work (which could conceivably be arranged by harnessing the motion of a semi-permeable membrane initially situated at the boundary between the liquids) the energy $T\Delta S$ for this process must, of course, come from outside as heat, if the temperature is to remain constant.

The lack of distortion on mixing, because of the similar sizes of the molecules, also means that there is no volume change on forming a perfect solution. Hence not only ΔU, but also ΔH, is zero; or the partial molar enthalpy of a component of a perfect solution is the same as the molar enthalpy in the pure liquid: $(h_i - h^\circ_i)$ is zero. Since $\mu_i = h_i - Ts_i$, and the difference in μ_i on mixing is $(\mu_i - \mu^\circ_i) = (h_i - h^\circ_i) - T(s_i - s^\circ_i)$, we have only the partial molar entropy to consider in calculating μ_i in a perfect solution.

§ 7.3 The entropy of perfect mixing

At this stage the entropy problem is fortunately very simple. There is no question of counting up all the possible ways of distributing the energy among the molecules, as would be required for a total entropy calculation, but only the ways of arranging the molecules on a lattice, which gives what is called the *configurational entropy*. All the other forms of entropy contribute equally to the pure components and to the solution, and so do not change on mixing.

Let there be N_A molecules of A and N_B molecules of B in a solution and consider the number of distinguishable ways of arranging them on a lattice of $(N_A + N_B)$ points. For simplicity regard the N_A and N_B molecules as all labelled in the first place. Then there are $(N_A + N_B)$ ways of choosing the occupant of the first site, but once this has been chosen $(N_A + N_B - 1)$ ways of choosing the occupant of the second site from among those left, $(N_A + N_B - 2)$ of choosing the third and so on until only one site remains and only one molecule remains to fill it. Any way of filling the first site can be combined with any of the $(N_A + N_B - 1)$ ways of filling the second and so on, so that the total number of ways of arranging the labelled molecules is

$$(N_A + N_B)(N_A + N_B - 1)(N_A + N_B - 2) \ldots$$
$$\times 2 \times 1 = (N_A + N_B)!$$

But all these arrangements would not actually be physically distinguishable, since the molecules are not really recognizable individually by labels: we only know which are of type A and which are of type B. Accordingly, every distinguishable arrangement must have been counted $N_A!N_B!$ times, which is the number of ways N_A labelled molecules can be arranged among themselves multiplied by the similar number for the B molecules (each arrangement of the A being combinable with any of the B arrangements).

The correct probability weight for the configurational entropy of the solution is therefore

$$\mathscr{P}_{\text{config}} = (N_A + N_B)!/N_A! \, N_B! \qquad (7.4)$$

The corresponding entropy contribution is given by equation (4.11) as

$$S_{\text{config}}/k = \ln \left[(N_A + N_B)!/N_A! \, N_B!\right]. \qquad (7.5)$$

Now consider how the configurational entropy of the whole solution changes on adding the last A molecule required to bring the number up to N_A. The final value is given by (7.5) and the initial value by a similar formula with $(N_A - 1)$ replacing N_A.

i.e. $$\frac{\Delta S_{\text{config}}}{k} = \ln \frac{(N_A + N_B)!}{N_A! \, N_B!} - \ln \frac{(N_A + N_B - 1)!}{(N_A - 1)! \, N_B!}$$

$$= \ln \frac{(N_A + N_B)!}{(N_A + N_B - 1)!} - \ln \frac{N_A!}{(N_A - 1)!}$$

$$= \ln (N_A + N_B) - \ln N_A$$

$$= -\ln x_A \qquad (7.6)$$

where the mole fraction of A in the solution, viz. $N_A/(N_A + N_B)$, is conveniently represented by x_A. Hence

$$\Delta S_{\text{config}} \text{ per mole of A} = -kN_0 \ln x_A = -R \ln x_A \quad (7.7)$$

(N_0 is the number of molecules in a mole.)

But the total change in entropy of the solution on adding one mole of A to a large enough quantity is the partial molar entropy of A, and the part of this sensitive to concentration is given by the process just described. The mole will also naturally carry with it into the solution its own standard entropy, $s°_A$, built up from thermal energy distributions, etc., so the complete expression for the partial molar entropy of A in the solution reads

$$s_A = s°_A - R \ln x_A \qquad (7.8)$$

The similar formula for s_B is derived in exactly the same way, and the total entropy of the solution is

$$S = n_A s_A + n_B s_B$$
$$= n_A s°_A + n_B s°_B - R[n_A \ln n_A + x_B \ln x_B] \quad (7.9)$$

Division by the total number of moles $(n_A + n_B)$ gives the mean molar entropy of the solution

$$s = x_A s°_A + x_B s°_B - R[x_A \ln x_A + x_B \ln x_B] \quad (7.10)$$

and subtraction of the entropies of the pure components gives what is called the mean molar entropy of mixing:

$$\Delta s_{mix} = -R[x_A \ln x_A + x_B \ln x_B] \qquad (7.11)$$

Since x_A and x_B are less than 1, this is positive.

The extension of all these equations to more than two components is straightforward.

§ 7.4 Chemical potentials in a perfect solution

Because $(\mu_i - \mu°_i)$ in a perfect solution is equal to $-T(s_i - s°_i)$, equation (7.8) gives directly

$$\mu_i = \mu°_i + RT \ln x_i \qquad (7.12)$$

Compare this with the definition of activity (on the rational scale):

$$\mu_i = \mu°_i + RT \ln a_i \qquad (2.15)$$

On the rational scale therefore, (setting $a_i = 1$ when $x_i = 1$), the activity of a substance in a perfect solution is equal to its mole fraction. A very simple property then follows immediately from (7.1):

$$p_i = x_i p^\circ_i \qquad (7.13)$$

The vapour pressure of a constituent of a perfect solution is proportional to its mole fraction. This is called Raoult's law and is usually taken as the thermodynamic definition of a perfect solution. From § 7.3 it follows that solutions composed of molecules of about the same size with similar intermolecular forces should obey Raoult's law, (7.13), fairly well over the whole composition range.

When better information is lacking, (7.12) can be used to allow roughly for the effect of dilution of a substance upon its chemical potential in a real solution, and a formula like (2.16) with mole fractions in place of activities is sometimes useful.

In *any* mixture, when one constituent (the 'solvent') is in large excess, the molecules of the other (the 'solute') are isolated from one another most of the time and are therefore in a constant environment made up of solvent molecules alone. The vapour pressure of a solute species consequently always tends towards proportionality with its mole fraction as the concentration is diminished, although the different molecular environment makes the proportionality constant in (7.13) differ from p°_i, the vapour pressure of the pure substance. The solute is then said to obey Henry's law and its chemical potential is of the form (7.12) with $\mu^\ominus_i$ in place of μ°_i. A solution in which Henry's law is obeyed is described as *ideal*, the perfect solution being a special case of an ideal solution.

In ionic solutions the forces are effective over several molecular diameters, and high dilutions are necessary before ideality is approached. There are also at least two different species involved, the cations and the anions, and Henry's law must then be applied correctly. For example, acetic acid dissociates progressively on dilution with water until finally the hydrogen and acetate ion concentrations both approximate to the analytical acid concentration. The partial pressure of acetic acid over the solution, while still proportional to the (very small) concentration of the species CH_3COOH in accordance with Henry's law, is then nevertheless proportional to the *square* of the total acid concentration, since the chemical equilibrium requires the concentration of CH_3COOH to be proportional to the product of the hydrogen and acetate ion concentrations.

§ 7.5 Activity coefficients

Deviations from ideal behaviour are expressed in terms of activity coefficients. On the *rational scale* the rational activity coefficient f_i is defined as

$$f_i = a_i/x_i \qquad (7.14)$$

Clearly f_i must tend to unity as x_i tends to 1, since the activity scale is fixed by setting $a_i = 1$ when $x_i = 1$.

Solutions are said to show positive deviations from Raoult's law when $f_i > 1$ and negative deviations when $f_i < 1$.

By (7.1) and (7.14) activity coefficients can be obtained directly from vapour pressure measurements:

$$f_i = p_i/p^\circ_i x_i \qquad (7.15)$$

For dilute solutions the *molal scale* is often used. The *molality* of a solute is the number of moles of the solute per kilogram of solvent: it is represented by the symbol m. Like the mole fraction, and unlike the molarity (moles per litre of solution), the molality of a solution does not vary with the temperature. If m_1 is the solvent molality, i.e. 1,000/(solvent molecular weight), the relationship between the molality of the solute 2 and its mole fraction is

$$x_2 = m_2/(m_1 + m_2) \qquad (7.16)$$

and for sufficiently dilute solutions this approximates closely to m_2/m_1. Thus in dilute solutions the molality is proportional to the mole fraction, and an *ideal solute* obeys the equation

$$\mu_i = \mu^\ominus_i + RT \ln m_i \qquad (7.17)$$

The symbol $\mu^\ominus_i$ is used as before to emphasize the difference between this standard state and the pure component used for the rational scale.

The molal activity coefficient γ_i is defined as

$$\gamma_i = a_i/m_i \qquad (7.18)$$

and the scale is fixed by making a_i approach m_i as the solution approaches infinite dilution: as $m_i \longrightarrow 0$, $a_i \longrightarrow m_i$ and $\gamma_i \longrightarrow 1$. This introduces a subtlety into the meaning of the standard state for the molal scale:

$$\mu_i = \mu^\ominus_i + RT \ln m_i\gamma_i \qquad (7.19)$$

Even for an ideal solute the region of applicability of (7.17) is strictly limited, since the numerical approximation on which it is based would break down for most solvents before a concentration of 1 molal was reached. The reference state is actually reached by an extrapolation up to 1 molal of the dependence of the properties on molality at much greater dilutions. For the same reason, γ_i in concentrated solutions does not simply reflect the deviations from perfect behaviour: it also incorporates the numerical effect of omitting m_2 from the denominator of (7.16).

§ 7.6 Osmotic coefficients

In dilute solution work the molal scale is used for solutes and the rational scale for the solvent. (This is equivalent to putting the 'constant solvent concentration' equal to unity in equilibrium formulae.) Because the solvent mole fraction and activity depart so little from unity, the rational activity coefficient of the solvent also remains very close to unity, and is therefore not such a good indicator of deviations from ideal behaviour as the solute activity coefficient.

Numbers for the solvent similar to solute activity coefficients are, however, obtained by taking the coefficient outside the logarithmic term:

$$\ln a_1 = g_1 \ln x_1 \qquad (7.20)$$

a_1 and x_1 are the solvent activity and mole fraction, and g_1 is the *rational osmotic coefficient*.

If each solute has a molality of m_i and gives rise to ν_i particles in solution (e.g. $\nu = 2$ for NaCl and 3 for CaCl$_2$), and m_1 is the solvent molality (1,000/[molecular weight]), the *molal osmotic coefficient* ϕ is defined by

$$\ln a_1 = -\phi(\sum_i \nu_i m_i)/m_1 \qquad (7.21)$$

Equilibrium data for solutions are often tabulated in terms of osmotic and activity coefficients because of the historical interest in testing interionic attraction theories. The solvent activity can always be obtained from such tables by (7.21). (For concentrated solutions a_1 tables would probably now be of more general use in practice than ϕ tables.)

§ 7.7 Real solutions

Unequal shapes and sizes of molecules upset the simple counting for (7.4), and so tend to produce departures from the perfect entropy of mixing. Unequal intermolecular forces, on the other hand, give rise to energy changes in mixing, and therefore spoil the simple identification of $-T(s_i - s°_i)$ with $(\mu_i - \mu°_i)$ which leads to (7.12). In general, differences in interaction energy between molecules of different types must affect not only the heat but also the entropy of mixing, since not all the possible distributions of molecules counted in (7.4) correspond to the same energy of the system. The complete explanation of the properties of all real solutions is therefore complex.

Nevertheless, solutions can be roughly and usefully classified in terms of molecular characteristics.

(a) Mixtures of *very similar molecules* of about the same size, such as mixtures of aliphatic hydrocarbons, tend to be perfect, and (7.12) is a good approximation. Molal Activity co-efficients always approach unity as the concentration is reduced, and all *dilute* solutions of ordinary non-electrolytes can therefore be treated as ideal without much error.

(b) Mixtures of molecules of similar type but of very different size, such as *solutions of polymers* in organic solvents, have practically no heat of mixing but usually have entropies of mixing very different from (7.11). Modifications of the argument of § 7.3, allowing for the occupation of several adjacent sites by a single polymer molecule, lead to the replacement of (7.11) by

$$\Delta s_{\text{mix}} = -R[x_A \ln \Phi_A + x_B \ln \Phi_B] \qquad (7.22)$$

where Φ_A and Φ_B are the volume fractions of A and B instead of the mole fractions. This formula explains very well the large deviations from Raoult's law found for rubber solutions, but is less successful in other cases.

(c) Mixtures of molecules of similar size but different short-range intermolecular forces in the pure liquids generally show both heats of mixing and specific entropy effects, but rational activity coefficients in binary systems of this kind can often be represented by the formulae

$$RT \ln f_A = Bx^2_B \qquad (7.23)$$
$$RT \ln f_B = Bx^2_A \qquad (7.24)$$

where the constant B has to be the same for both constituents to satisfy the Gibbs–Duhem equation (6.13).

If B turns out to be independent of the temperature it follows from the equation

$$\partial(\mu_i - \mu^\circ_i)/\partial T = -(s_i - s^\circ_i) \qquad (7.25)$$

that the deviations represented by (7.23) and (7.24) contribute nothing to the entropy of mixing, which therefore has the perfect value (7.11). Solutions with this property of perfect entropy but non-zero heat of mixing are called *regular solutions*.

The magnitude of B can often be estimated approximately from properties of the pure components, using Hildebrand's tables of δ, the 'solubility parameter'. For a dilute solution of a solute with solubility parameter δ_2 and molar volume v°_2,

$$B \simeq v^\circ_2(\delta_1 - \delta_2)^2 \qquad (7.26)$$

δ_1 being the solubility parameter, of the solvent. δ is related to the energy of formation of a cavity in the pure substance and so is a measure of the intermolecular forces or 'internal pressure': it is estimated empirically from the energy of vaporization (i.e. the enthalpy, l_v, less RT) by the formula

$$\delta_i = [(l_v - RT)/v^\circ_i]^{\frac{1}{2}} \qquad (7.27)$$

The vapour pressures corresponding to (7.23) and (7.24) satisfy the equations

$$\ln (p_A/p^\circ_A) = \ln (1 - x_B) + (B/RT)x^2_B \qquad (7.28)$$
$$\ln (p_B/p^\circ_B) = \ln (1 - x_A) + (B/RT)x^2_A \qquad (7.29)$$

As the value of B in these equations is increased, the positive deviations from Raoult's law become larger until a point is reached at which the equations would actually predict a maximum in each vapour pressure (and chemical potential) at $x_A = x_B = 0.5$. But a single solution of this composition would decrease in free energy spontaneously by splitting into two phases with different compositions. Such phases can still be at equilibrium because μ for each constituent can be the same for compositions on either side of the maximum. (Shaking up water with ether gives rise to two phases, one rich in water and the other rich in ether, but you cannot tell which is which simply by smelling them after separation, as both have the same ether vapour pressure.) By differentiation of (7.28) or (7.29), the maximum value of B consistent with a single phase is found to be $2RT$ (for solutions obeying these equations strictly). At room temperature this would correspond to a difference in δ values of about 3 or 4 units; and one would therefore expect a pair of liquids with a difference of this kind to show some tendency to split into two phases. The molecular interpretation is that groups of like molecules then pack together with much less energy than groups of unlike molecules, and the entropy of mixing and the thermal kinetic energy are not large enough to outweigh this effect in certain regions of composition.

Activity coefficients can be approximately represented by (7.23) for a large class of common non-electrolyte solutions, such as mixtures of organic solvents, and solutions in these of iodine, sulphur and other inorganic substances. The equation has also been found to hold in metal alloy systems, and even in some mixtures containing hydroxylic substances, although these differ from ordinary non-electrolytes in their ability to form strongly directed hydrogen bonds.

(d) In *electrolytic solutions* there are long-range electrostatic forces between the ions, which give rise to marked non-ideality even at quite high dilutions. Because of the presence of these forces, the distribution around any particular ion cannot be as random as would be required for the counting which leads to the perfect entropy of mixing: a given ion tends to have more ions of opposite than of the same sign in its vicinity. The ions must therefore have a negative electrostatic potential energy relative to the reference at infinite dilution (infinite separation), which accounts for the non-ideal contribution to the chemical potential, $RT \ln \gamma$.

Ionic solutions always contain anions and cations together; so the chemical potentials of single ions are never measured, only combinations of them. The chemical potential of sodium chloride in solution is

$$\mu_{NaCl} = \mu_{Na^+} + \mu_{Cl^-} = \mu^{\ominus}_{Na} + \mu^{\ominus}_{Cl^-} + RT \ln (a_{Na^+} \times a_{Cl^-})$$

of calcium chloride

$$\mu_{CaCl_2} = \mu^{\ominus}{}_{Ca^{++}} + 2\mu^{\ominus}{}_{Cl^-} + RT \ln (a_{Ca^{++}} \times a^2{}_{Cl^-})$$

and of a salt $M_{\nu^+}X_{\nu^-}$

$$\mu = \nu_+\mu^{\ominus}{}_+ + \nu_-\mu^{\ominus}{}_- + RT \ln (a_+{}^{\nu_+} \times a_-{}^{\nu_-}) \quad (7.30)$$

$$= \mu^{\ominus} + RT \ln (m_+{}^{\nu_+}m_-{}^{\nu_-}) + RT \ln (\gamma_+{}^{\nu_+}\gamma_-{}^{\nu_-}) \quad (7.31)$$

The numbers of ions of each type in the molecular formula appear as multiples in the chemical potentials, and hence as powers in the activities due to the logarithmic form.

Because of the appearance of the ionic activities in these combinations whenever the overall chemical potential of a salt is required, *mean ionic quantities*, $a_{\pm}, m_{\pm}$ and $\gamma_{\pm}$, are defined. For the salt $M_{\nu_+}X_{\nu_-}$

$$a = a_{\pm}{}^{\nu} = a_+{}^{\nu_+}a_-{}^{\nu_-} \quad (7.32)$$

$$m_{\pm}{}^{\nu} = m_+{}^{\nu_+}m_-{}^{\nu_-} \quad (7.33)$$

$$\gamma_{\pm} = \gamma_+{}^{\nu_+}\gamma_-{}^{\nu_-} \quad (7.34)$$

ν is written for $\nu_+ + \nu_-$, the number of ions per molecule, and m_+ and m_- are, of course, known from the salt molality and the numbers ν_+ and ν_-. (Similar expressions can be set up for the molar scale.) Defined in this way, the mean ionic and the ionic quantities still satisfy the formula (7.18). (7.31) can now be written more simply as

$$\mu = \mu^{\ominus} + \nu RT \ln m_{\pm} + \nu RT \ln \gamma_{\pm} \quad (7.35)$$

For example, the chemical potential of fully dissociated HCl in solution is

$$\mu_{HCl} = \mu^{\ominus}{}_{HCl} + 2RT \ln m + 2RT \ln \gamma_{\pm} \quad (7.36)$$

the salt molality m being the same as both m_+ and m_- in this case.

Most common electrolytes, although completely ionized, are,

however, incompletely dissociated in solution, in the sense that pairs or clusters of ions exist in appreciable quantities even at concentrations of 10^{-2} molal or less in solvents of high permittivity (dielectric constant) like water. The only completely dissociated electrolytes are those with large ions of low charge, like the halides of the alkali metals; polyvalent and small ions tend to form ion pairs.

Where ion association occurs, equation (7.35) can be regarded in two ways. On the one hand, all strong electrolyte $\gamma_\pm$ data are calculated for the tables in terms of the completely dissociated reference and the 'stoichiometric' $\gamma_\pm$ is given directly by (7.35) as it stands, with the m_+ and m_- of (7.33) interpreted simply as $\nu_+ m$ and $\nu_- m$. On the other hand, for the understanding and interpretation of these experimental $\gamma_\pm$ quantities, attention is fixed on the 'free' ions (i.e. those not present as pairs or clusters), for which the true molalities are less than $\nu_+ m$ and $\nu_- m$. Since the free and associated forms of the electrolyte are in equilibrium, its chemical potential must be the same whether it is thought of in terms of the free-energy change on adding a mole in the form in which the ions actually exist, partially free, partially associated, or in terms of the free-energy change on adding the free ions only:

$$\mu = \mu^\ominus + RT \ln (m_+{}^{\nu_+} m_-{}^{\nu_-}) + RT \ln (f_+{}^{\nu_+} f_-{}^{\nu_-}) \quad (7.37)$$

Here m_+ and m_- are the true molalities of the free ions and the symbol f is adopted for the molal activity coefficients of the free ion species to distinguish them clearly from the stoichiometric quantities γ. (Confusion with the rational activity coefficient is unlikely.) Since m_+ and m_- are less than $m\nu_+$ and $m\nu_-$, $f_\pm$ is larger than $\gamma_\pm$ when there is ion association.

Ionic activity coefficients depend upon the total ionic environment, as would be expected from the nature of the long-range electrostatic forces involved in electrolytic solutions. A given ion's contribution to this environment depends upon both its molality, m_i, and its charge, z_i (in electron units:

$z_i = +1$ for Na^+, -2 for SO_4^{2-}), and both effects are allowed for in the definition of the *ionic strength*, I:

$$I = \tfrac{1}{2}\sum_i m_i z_i^2 \qquad (7.38)$$

as defined empirically by G. N. Lewis. (Theoretically a definition in molar terms is preferable, but the difference is very small for dilute *aqueous* solutions.) Where ion association occurs the summation is taken to refer to all the true concentrations of the species as they actually occur, the ion pairs being treated as single ions with a net charge equal to the algebraic sum, $z_+ + z_-$. An electrolyte has approximately the same mean ionic activity coefficient in all solutions of the same ionic strength.

According to the interionic attraction theory,

$$\log_{10} f_{\pm} = -\frac{A \mid z_+ z_- \mid I^{\frac{1}{2}}}{1 + B\mathring{a}I^{\frac{1}{2}}} + bI \qquad (7.39)$$

A and B are theoretical constants which depend upon the temperature and the permittivity of the solvent and $\mathring{a}$ is the distance of closest approach of the ions expressed in Ångstrom units. The constant b is empirical and incorporates allowances for a number of effects which give a linear dependence of $\log_{10} f_{\pm}$ on the ionic strength at moderate concentrations.

For very dilute aqueous solutions (10^{-2} molal or less) a first approximation to an ionic activity coefficient, f_i, at 25°C is obtained from the limiting formula

$$\log_{10} f_i = -0.509 z_i^2 I^{\frac{1}{2}} \qquad (7.40)$$

A better approximation for ionic strengths up to 0·1 is the empirical form

$$\log_{10} f_i = -0.5 z_i^2 \left\{ \frac{I^{\frac{1}{2}}}{1 + I^{\frac{1}{2}}} - 0.3I \right\} \qquad (7.41)$$

This form takes advantage of the fact that $B\mathring{a}$ is approximately unity, and any slight differences of $(1 + I^{\frac{1}{2}})$ from $(1 + B\mathring{a}I^{\frac{1}{2}})$

are automatically taken up in the linear term bI (because the inverse of $1 + kI^{\frac{1}{2}}$ is approximately $1 - kI^{\frac{1}{2}}$).

For accurate work on particular electrolytes the form (7.39) is used, while (7.41) has wide applications in problems involving many ionic species, including ion pairs, for which detailed information is just not available. In all cases it is true, however, that the activity coefficient of an ionic species in dilute solution depends principally upon its charge type (z_i) and the total ionic strength.

§ 7.8 Ionic equilibria in solution

All the following equilibria involve ionic activity coefficients.

(To avoid clumsy suffixes activities are indicated by round, ( ), and molalities by square, [ ], brackets.)

Acid dissociation:

$$NH_4^+ \text{ (aq)} = NH_3 \text{ (aq)} + H^+ \text{ (aq)} \qquad (7.42)$$
$$K_a = (NH_3)(H^+)/(NH_4^+)$$
$$= \frac{[NH_3][H^+]}{[NH_4^+]} \times \frac{f_u \times f_I}{f_I} \qquad (7.43)$$

Acid dissociation:

$$CH_3COOH \text{ (aq)} = CH_3COO^- \text{ (aq)} + H^+ \text{ (aq)} \qquad (7.44)$$
$$K_a = (CH_3COO^-)(H^+)/(CH_3COOH)$$
$$= \frac{[CH_3COO^-][H^+]}{[CH_3COOH]} \times \frac{f_I \times f_I}{f_u} \qquad (7.45)$$

Dissociation of an ion pair:

$$CaFe(CN)_6^{2-} \text{ (aq)} = Ca^{2+} \text{ (aq)} + Fe(CN)_6^{4-} \text{ (aq)} \qquad (7.46)$$
$$K = (Ca^{2+})(Fe(CN)_6^{4-})/CaFe(CN)_6^{2-}$$
$$= \frac{[Ca^{2+}][Fe(CN)_6^{4-}]}{[CaFe(CN)_6^{2-}]} \times \frac{f_{II} \times f_{IV}}{f_{II}} \qquad (7.47)$$

To a good approximation, the activity coefficients of ions at a given ionic strength depend only on their charge-types, in accordance with (7.41); so they need only be characterized by the charge-type as a subscript, as f_I, f_{II}, f_{IV}. It is also a good approximation in dilute solution to set the activity coefficient of an uncharged species, f_u, at unity. (Actually $\log_{10} f_u$ shows a very small linear dependence on the ionic strength.)

Application of these principles shows immediately that for equilibria like (7.42) the activity coefficients cancel out in dilute solution; the position of equilibrium is therefore hardly affected at all by the addition of 'neutral salts' which simply increase the ionic strength.

Both (7.44) and (7.46), on the other hand, are quite sensitive to the ionic strength. If m is the overall molality of acetic acid and α its degree of dissociation (7.45) can be transformed to

$$\log_{10} K_a = \log_{10} \alpha^2 m/(1 - \alpha) - \left\{ \frac{I^{\frac{1}{2}}}{1 + I^{\frac{1}{2}}} - 0.3 I \right\} \quad (7.48)$$

The corresponding formula for (7.47) has eight times this ionic strength contribution because of the activity coefficient of a 4-valent ion which remains uncancelled.

In many practical problems of this kind a short series of successive approximations is required because the activity coefficients depend upon the ionic strength, which is not known accurately until the degree of dissociation is known.

Sometimes the experimental conditions affect the meaning of 'salt effects'. The dissociation of a protonated species as determined by spectrophotometry, which measures the concentrations of the protonated and unprotonated species, would not be much affected (in dilute solutions) by the addition of neutral salts, as explained above; but the ratio of the two species would be affected by the presence of salts if the pH of the solution were adjusted throughout to the same value as given by a pH-meter and glass electrode assembly. The reason is that the glass electrode measures $-\log_{10} [H^+] f_I$ approximately rather than $-\log_{10}$- [H$^+$] and so removes the convenient cancellation of f_1 in (7.43).

Further work

Read E. A. Guggenheim, *Thermodynamics* (North-Holland, 2nd edition, 1950), pp. 208–214, or E. F. Caldin, *Chemical Thermodynamics* (O.U.P., 1958), Chapter 11.

An authoritative account of *non-electrolyte solutions* is given by J. H. Hildebrand and R. L. Scott, *The Solubility of Non-electrolytes* (Reinhold, 3rd edition, 1950). Look at the magnitudes of the solubility parameters in the Appendix.

Read pp. 1–5 in *Ion Association* by C. W. Davies (Butterworth, 1962). This is the source of formula (7.41).

Read pp. 174–183 and 229–233 of *Electrolyte Solutions*, by R. A. Robinson and R. H. Stokes (Butterworth, 2nd edition, 1959).

For arguments like § 7.3, avoiding Stirling's theorem, see *J. Chem. Educ.*, 1962, **39**, 27, and for the effects of vapour equilibria on (7.2), *Trans. Faraday Soc.*, 1954, **50**, 352.

Problems for Chapter 7

1. Show that the equations

$$\mu_1 = \mu^\circ_1 - RT \ln x_1$$
$$\mu_2 = \mu^\circ_2 + RT \ln x_2$$

satisfy the Gibbs–Duhem condition by proving that

$$\frac{d\mu_1}{dx_2} = -\frac{x_2}{x_1}\frac{d\mu_2}{dx_2}$$

2. (*a*) Show that the Gibbs–Duhem equation can be reduced to the following form between the rational activity coefficients:

$$x_1 \frac{d \ln f_1}{dx_2} = -x_2 \frac{d \ln f_2}{dx_2}$$

(b) Using this formula, test the consistency of equations (7.23) and (7.24).

3. (a) Determine the activity coefficient of thallium (a_1/x_1) in alloys with tin having a thallium mole fraction of x_1 from the following e.m.f. data, using the formula $E = (RT/F) \ln (1/a_1)$. (T is in $^\circ$K and F is the faraday.)

x_1	0·1030	0·2685	0·3722	0·6714
E at 352°C (volts)	0·0776	0·0418	0·0314	0·0155
E at 478°C (volts)	0·1097	0·0604	0·0462	0·0210

(From J. H. Hildebrand and J. N. Sharma, *J. Amer. Chem. Soc.*, 1929, **51**, 462.)

(b) Plot the logarithms of the activity coefficients against x_2^2 at each temperature to test the validity of the expression

$$RT \ln f_1 = Bx_2^2$$

(c) Calculate a_1 and a_2 at x_1 values of 0·1, 0·2, 0·5, 0·8 and 0·9 and plot them against x_1. Is the variation with temperature of the deviation from ideality in the expected direction?

4. The vapour pressure of pure liquid butane (p°_2) at 25°C is 1,823 mm Hg. Calculate the partial pressure (p_2) of butane over a solution in benzene in which the mole fraction of butane (x_2) is 0·2: (a) assuming perfect behaviour, and (b) using the δ tables of Hildebrand and Scott (Appendix 1).

These δ values give B directly in cal mole^{-1} when v is in cm^3 in equation (7.26). Since the solution is rather concentrated, take the average of the molar volume of benzene, $v^\circ_1 = 89$ cm^3, and butane, $v^\circ_2 = 101$ cm^3, for v° in (7.26).

Comment on the results of (a) and (b) in the light of the knowledge that the experimental value of p_2 is actually 640 mm Hg. (G. Calingaert and L. H. Hitchcock, *J. Amer. Chem. Soc.*, 1927, **49**, 750.)

5. Find values for the equilibrium constants at 25°C of the

reactions (7.42), (7.44) and (7.46) from *Stability Constants for Metal-Ion Complexes* (the Chemical Society Special Publications, Nos. 6 and 7, or 17), where the constants are expressed as 'formation constants' (the opposite of dissociation constants) and in 'metal-ligand' language. For NH_4^+, for example, the 'metal' is H^+ and the 'ligand' NH_3.

The logarithm of the K value is recorded as K for short. This is a different convention from pK, which is the *negative* logarithm of K.

If in doubt about the meaning of a constant, confirm your interpretation by consulting the literature reference in the table.

6. From the value of K for (7.46), use (7.47) and (7.41) to calculate the fraction of cyanoferrate(II), which exists as ion pairs in a $0.01\,M$ solution of the pure calcium salt, $Ca_2Fe(CN)_6$.

(First of all write down the amounts of the various ions present in terms of m and α, the fraction of cyanoferrate in the associated form. Then formulate the ionic strength and K in these terms and begin successive approximations for $\dfrac{(1 - \alpha)}{\alpha}$, guessing first $\alpha \simeq 0.8$ for I and the insensitive $(2 - \alpha)$ term involved in the formula.

Don't carry too many places of decimals: the calculation is only approximate, and the function $I^{\frac{1}{2}}/(1 + I^{\frac{1}{2}})$ can be read off a slide-rule quite easily, using the ordinary and square scales and taking care with the position of the decimal point.)

8

Phase Equilibrium

§ 8.1 Revision

The chemical potential of any substance which is free to pass from one phase to another has to be the same in the two phases at equilibrium (§ 1.4). To formulate the maintenance of equilibrium between phases when conditions are changed therefore, a knowledge of the variation of chemical potentials with temperature, pressure and composition is required. The appropriate equations are:

$$\left(\frac{\partial \mu_i}{\partial T}\right)_P = -s_i \tag{6.27}$$

or
$$\left(\frac{\partial (\mu_i/T)}{\partial T}\right)_P = -\frac{h_i}{T^2} \tag{6.29}$$

$$\left(\frac{\partial \mu_i}{\partial P}\right)_T = v_i \tag{6.28}$$

$$\left(\frac{\partial \mu_i}{\partial \ln a_i}\right)_{P,\,T} = RT \qquad \text{from (2.15)}$$

or
$$\left(\frac{\partial (\mu_i/T)}{\partial \ln a_i}\right)_{P,\,T} = R \qquad \text{from (2.15)}$$

§ 8.2 The degrees of freedom in a system of more than one phase

A *phase* is a homogeneous region of matter (such as solid, liquid or gas) separated from other regions by a boundary surface. Regions of identical composition and structure, such as two lumps of ice, count as the same phase; but regions of the same composition but different structure (ice and water) are different phases.

According to equation (6.1) there are $c + 2$ degrees of freedom in a c-component single-phase system which can be varied in total amount. You may feel at first that these degrees of freedom could correspond to the $c + 2$ variables T, P and the μ_i. Notice, however, that the μ_i would not give as complete information as the n_i, since a specification of T, P and all the μ_i would give no indication of the bulk of the phase, for the μ_i would only fix the relative magnitudes of the n_i. This must mean that T, P and the μ_i only give $(c + 2) - 1$ independent variables, or in other words that changes in all but one of these quantities fix the changes in the remaining one. The quantitative condition linking the variables in this way has already been deduced:

$$-S\mathrm{d}T + V\mathrm{d}P = \sum_i n_i \mathrm{d}\mu_i \qquad (6.12)$$

When the conditions necessary for the coexistence of phases are required the total bulk of each phase is beside the point. For example, at atmospheric pressure ice and water coexist at $0°C$, no matter how much ice and water may be present. (Experimentally it is usually necessary to have enough ice to ensure that thermal equilibrium is attained, but this does not affect the essential argument.) In this kind of enquiry the $(c + 2) - 1$ variables are evidently sufficient to fix the (intensive) characteristics of a single phase.

Now suppose that a new phase is formed out of some or all of the c components. At equilibrium the T, P and μ_i must be the same in both the original and the new phase, and at first sight it may appear that $(c + 2) - 1$ of these variables have still to be specified for a complete description of the whole system. But remember that the 1 was subtracted because of the relationship (6.12) for the first phase. The next stage is to recognize that there must be another, *different* equation of the type (6.12) for each new phase added: i.e. if there are two phases, $F = (c + 2) - 2$, if there are three, $F = (c + 2) - 3$, and so on. If the number of phases is represented by P therefore,

$$F = c + 2 - P \qquad (8.1)$$

This is known as the *Phase Rule* of Willard Gibbs. Notice that the equations (6.12) *must* be different for the new phases added, because any two regions having the $c + 2$ coefficients, S, V and n_i, in identical proportions in (6.12) would be identical phases.

Since in most applications of the phase rule some of the components are absent from one or more of the phases, it is emphasized that (6.12) for each additional phase always reduces the degrees of freedom by one, whatever the number of $n_i d\mu_i$ terms involved, as it always gives one more of the variables in terms of the others. For the special (and common) case in which one of the phases contains only a single component, μ_i for that component is fixed by the temperature and pressure, not only in the pure phase itself but, at equilibrium, in all the coexistent phases. This is consistent with reducing F by 1 in accordance with the rule, just as for a phase in which all the components are present.

§ 8.3 The degrees of freedom in a one-component system

By the phase rule, when $c = 1$, $F = 3 - P$. Thus the maximum number of coexistent phases possible in a one-component system is 3, and these can only coexist at one temperature and one pressure, since the system then has no degrees of freedom at all. It is said to be *invariant* in this condition. If heat is absorbed by such a system the phase of lowest entropy diminishes in bulk at the expense of the other two, but the equilibrium temperature and pressure cannot change until this phase finally disappears and only two phases are left.

With two phases the system is *univariant* ($F = 1$), and this means that within the region of stability of the phases if a certain temperature is chosen the equilibrium pressure is also thereby fixed. Addition of heat to such a system increases the temperature and pressure together in a way that depends upon the particular properties of the system. Thus one can speak of the vapour pressure of a liquid at a certain temperature, for example.

A single isolated phase of one component is bivariant: e.g. both the temperature and the pressure have to be given to specify the state of a gas completely.

§ 8.4 Quantitative expressions for the connexions between T and P in a one-component system

For bivariant systems, the connexion between the temperature, pressure and one other variable is an *equation of state*, the simplest example of which is (2.5) for a perfect gas.

In the case of a one-component univariant system, there are two phases, to each of which equations (6.27) and (6.28) apply. Initially the two phases α and β are in equilibrium so that $^\alpha\mu = {}^\beta\mu$. If the system is to remain in equilibrium after changing the temperature by dT and the pressure by dP, the consequent changes in $^\alpha\mu$ and $^\beta\mu$ must be equal to keep these two quantities the same:

$$
\begin{bmatrix} \text{Change in } ^\alpha\mu \text{ due} \\ \text{to change in } T \end{bmatrix} + \begin{bmatrix} \text{Change in } ^\alpha\mu \text{ due} \\ \text{to change in } P \end{bmatrix}
$$
$$
= \begin{bmatrix} \text{Change in } ^\beta\mu \text{ due} \\ \text{to change in } T \end{bmatrix} + \begin{bmatrix} \text{Change in } ^\beta\mu \text{ due} \\ \text{to change in } P \end{bmatrix}
$$

The change in μ in each case is equal to the rate of change of μ with the variable multiplied by the actual change in the variable. Hence, in symbols,

$$\frac{\partial^\alpha \mu}{\partial T}\,\mathrm{d}T + \frac{\partial^\alpha \mu}{\partial P}\,\mathrm{d}P = \frac{\partial^\beta \mu}{\partial T}\,\mathrm{d}T + \frac{\partial^\beta \mu}{\partial P}\,\mathrm{d}P \qquad (8.2)$$

i.e. $$-{}^\alpha s\,\mathrm{d}T + {}^\alpha v\,\mathrm{d}P = -{}^\beta s\,\mathrm{d}T + {}^\beta v\,\mathrm{d}P \qquad (8.3)$$

$$\frac{\mathrm{d}P}{\mathrm{d}T} = \frac{\Delta s}{\Delta v} = \frac{l}{T\Delta v} \qquad (8.4)$$

Here $\Delta s = {}^\beta s - {}^\alpha s$, $\Delta v = {}^\beta v - {}^\alpha v$, $l = {}^\beta h - {}^\alpha h$, the entropy, volume and enthalpy changes on transferring a mole from phase α to phase β: the enthalpy change is the same as the molar latent heat of the transformation.

The three lines OA, OB and OC in Figure 8.1, which represent diagrammatically the phase equilibria between ice and vapour, water and vapour, and water and ice respectively, are all

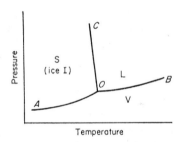

FIG. 8.1   Phase equilibrium diagram for water

determined by equation (8.4), with the l and Δv values appropriate to the various phase changes. (The S, L and V areas represent single-phase, bivariant systems.) OA and OB are called the vapour-pressure curves for ice and water, and OC is said to show the effect of pressure on the melting-point of ice. OC leans backwards because the Δv in (8.4) is negative in this special (and unusual) case: ice floats on water.

O is not at the normal melting temperature of ice, but at the *triple-point,* the invariant point at which all three phases are in equilibrium. P and T have therefore to satisfy three integrated forms of (8.4) simultaneously. The normal melting-point (0°C) lies along OC at the ordinate equal to the atmospheric pressure, where only the solid and liquid are in equilibrium, since the vapour pressure of the liquid at 0°C lies on BO produced to the left and therefore exceeds that of the solid which lies on OA.

Over moderate pressure ranges (8.4) is easily integrated for transitions between condensed phases since l and Δv can be regarded as practically constant. P then varies linearly with $\ln T$ or with T itself over small temperature ranges. (When necessary, allowances for compressibility and thermal expansion are not difficult to make.)

The volume of a mole of gas, on the other hand, is obviously very dependent on the pressure and the integration of (8.4) for vaporization and sublimation therefore looks very different. As an excellent approximation, the molar volume of the condensed phase can be ignored in comparison with that of the vapour, which is RT/P. Substitution for Δv in (8.4) then leads to the *Clapeyron–Clausius equation*:

$$\frac{\mathrm{d}\ln P}{\mathrm{d}T} = \frac{l}{RT^2} \qquad (8.5)$$

By ignoring the temperature dependence of l (easily allowed for by Δc_p), (8.5) is then integrated between T and T°, the normal sublimation- or boiling-point at which $P = P^\circ$:

$$\ln\left(\frac{P}{P^\circ}\right) = -\frac{l}{R}\left(\frac{1}{T} - \frac{1}{T^\circ}\right) \qquad (8.6)$$

A plot of the logarithm of the vapour pressure against $1/T$ is therefore nearly a straight line, the slope of which gives the mean l for the temperature range involved. Alternatively, if l and T° are known the vapour pressure can be calculated at the temperature T. For normal liquids, an approximate value of P is calculable even if only T° is known, since l is approximately

$21T°$ cal mole^{-1}. (See problem 5.5. Associated liquids, like water and the alcohols, have low entropies in the condensed phase, and hence show more than the normal entropy increase on vaporization.)

The full phase diagram for a single-component system is often more complex than Figure 8.1: even with H_2O, several different crystal forms of ice are encountered at high pressures, where there are several more triple points involving only condensed phases.

§ 8.5 The degrees of freedom in a two-component system

If $c = 2$, $F = 4 - P$. Invariant points are now possible with four coexistent phases (quadruple points), but most of the interest centres around conditions where fewer phases are in equilibrium. The extra degree of freedom often shows up in the ability to alter the concentration when the two components form solutions.

§ 8.6 Liquid–vapour equilibria in a two-component system

If the components form a single liquid solution there are two phases to consider, one liquid and one vapour: $F = 4 - 2 = 2$. Thus, at a given temperature and liquid composition (fixing the two degrees of freedom) the solution has a fixed vapour pressure. Quantitatively this equilibrium pressure is the sum of the vapour pressures of the two constituents of the solution as calculated from equations like (7.28) and (7.29).

On raising the temperature of the solution a point is reached at which the total equilibrium vapour pressure is equal to the pressure of the surrounding atmosphere and the liquid boils. In general, one constituent is more volatile than the other, and condensation of the vapour therefore produces a liquid richer in that substance. For example, Figure 8.2 shows the phase diagram for the A–B system at the fixed pressure of 1 atm. The point L_1 represents the boiling-point of a liquid rich in B, which yields a vapour at V_1 enriched in the more volatile A. Condensation of this produces the liquid which boils at L_2 yielding the vapour at V_2 and the new liquid at L_3, still further enriched in A, and so on. This is the principle of the separation of substances by *distillation*.

Instead of performing the successive distillations separately, the same effect can be produced by passing the vapour up a *fractionating column* down which the condensing liquid flows in counter-current. To get good mixing between the liquid and the vapour and thus approach the equilibrium distribution between the phases at each level, the column is packed with glass beads or helices, or is designed as a vertical series of 'bee-hive' shelves. Because of the enrichment in the more volatile constituent, the equilibrium temperature naturally decreases as the vapour passes up the column. The efficiency of fractionation is measured in terms of *theoretical plates*: a column yielding a final composition of L_3 (Figure 8.2) from an initial liquid L_1 is equivalent to two theoretical plates.

Even if the mixture is perfect so that the total pressure varies

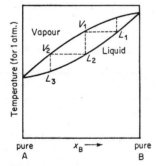

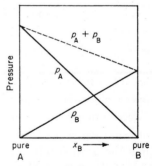

FIG. 8.2   Fixed pressure (variation of T with x)

FIG. 8.3   Fixed temperature (variation of P with x for a perfect solution)

linearly with the mole fraction (Figure 8.3), curved lines still appear on the constant pressure phase diagram (Figure 8.2) because the vapour pressures do not vary linearly with temperature but follow equations like (8.6.). (It is not difficult to show that the individual vapour pressures in a mixture, the p_i,

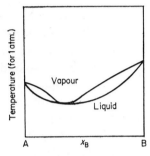

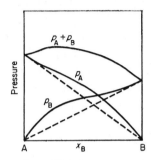

FIG. 8.4 Fixed pressure (solution with minimum b.p.)

FIG. 8.5 Fixed temperature (solution with maximum v.p.)

obey separate equations like (8.6), in which l_i has to be understood to mean the enthalpy in the gas less the partial molar enthalpy of i in the actual solution, which may often be very similar to that of the pure liquid. Remembering that μ_i/T for the vapour and the liquid have to be the same, differentiate (2.9) in the form $\mu_i/T = \mu^\circ{}_i/T + R \ln p_i$ with respect to temperature and apply (6.29) to the liquid on the left and to the vapour on the right.)

Positive deviations from Raoult's law can give rise to a maximum in the sum of the partial pressures at constant temperature (Figure 8.5), and hence to a minimum in the boiling-point curve (Figure 8.4). The distillates from solutions both to the right and to the left of this minimum always tend towards the composition having this low boiling-point, while the liquid from which the vapour is distilled tends towards one or other of the pure substances. (Mixtures of water and ethanol behave in this way.)

Large negative deviations can similarly give rise to a maximum boiling-mixture, to which the liquid composition tends while the vapour becomes enriched in one or other of the pure substances. (Solutions of the strong acids in water are examples.) Solutions having these minimum or maximum boiling-points are known as *azeotropes*.

More extreme positive deviations lead to the separation of the liquid into two phases over certain regions of composition (§ 7.7c), thus reducing F by 1. For the three phases to coexist at a fixed temperature therefore, the overall pressure and the compositions of the two liquid phases are completely determined, and alterations in the overall proportions of the compounds simply affect the relative amounts of the phases. If the liquids are subjected to the atmospheric pressure instead of their own vapour pressure the compositions of the phases are still fixed (though they may be very slightly altered by the new pressure), because although the vapour is no longer in equilibrium, thus leaving a two-phase system, the extra degree of freedom has already been taken up by fixing the pressure. Another way of expressing the same result is to say that the two liquids have definite mutual solubilities at a fixed temperature and pressure.

Since non-ideality is usually diminished by increasing the temperature, these systems sometimes revert to one phase at what is known as an *upper consolute temperature*: for phenol–water mixtures this occurs at 65·85°C. (Mixtures of water with triethylamine are anomalous in showing a lower consolute temperature.)

§ 8.7 Solid–liquid equilibria in a two-component system

In ordinary laboratory experiments on solubilities of solids or depressions of freezing-point, no attempt is made to bring the vapour into equilibrium and the overall pressure is simply allowed to remain at that of the atmosphere. For describing the conditions of equilibrium in such circumstances it is therefore only necessary to consider the solid and liquid phases and to regard one degree of freedom as already lost by fixing the pressure at ~ 1 atm. (Equilibria between condensed phases are in any case rather insensitive to pressure.) The remaining degrees of freedom, F', are then given by the expression

$$F' = C + 1 - P \qquad (8.7)$$

and for $C = 2$, $\qquad F' = 3 - P$

Figure 8.6 represents the simplest form of solid–liquid phase diagram, which can be built up from the information given by cooling A–B mixtures of various compositions. A sample cooling-curve is shown in Figure 8.7.

The liquefied mixture cools fairly rapidly first of all, but when one of the components begins to separate out as a solid the latent heat liberated reduces the rate of cooling. During the separation of one component in the solid form the liquid naturally becomes more concentrated in the other and a point is eventually reached at which this, too, separates out as a solid. There are then three phases, two solid and one liquid, and $F' = 0$. The temperature therefore remains stationary until all the liquid has disappeared, after which there is simple Newtonian cooling of a mixture of two types of crystals.

As $F' = 0$ when three phases are present, the temperature at which the horizontal part of the cooling-curve occurs must always be the same whatever the initial composition of the mixture, although the length of time spent at this temperature naturally depends on how much liquid is left to be solidified when it is reached. The duration of the 'halt' at this temperature is often recorded in experiments of this kind, as it helps to confirm the interpretation of the phase relations: the longest halt (for a series of samples of the same weight) is given by the sample of such a composition that on cooling the liquid no solid appears until both begin to separate out at once. This

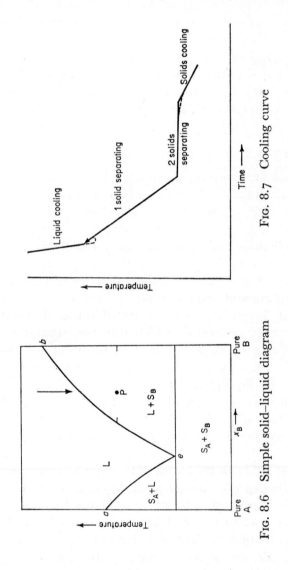

Fig. 8.7 Cooling curve

Fig. 8.6 Simple solid–liquid diagram

is known as the *eutectic* composition. Although a eutectic mixture solidifies at a fixed temperature, it is not a compound: its composition can be slightly altered by changing the pressure, and two forms of crystals can be distinguished under the microscope.

This type of investigation is known as *thermal analysis*. In practice, the cooling-curves usually show the irregularities indicated by dotted lines in Figure 8.7. The liquid usually supercools to some extent before the first separation of solid and, because of the difficulty of stirring the eutectic mixture adequately right up to the disappearance of the last trace of liquid, the curve usually rounds off towards the final solid line, the remaining liquid being insulated in pockets away from the thermometer. In both cases the true equilibrium form of the curve is obtained by extrapolation from the well-behaved regions, as in the continuous line on the diagram.

On Figure 8.6 there are three points, *a*, *b* and *e*, at which liquids solidify completely at fixed temperatures, but two of these, *a* and *b*, correspond to pure 1-component systems: the third is the eutectic. The lines *ae* and *be* represent the temperatures at which solid first separates from cooling liquids of the compositions represented by the corresponding points along the base-line: along *ae* solid A separates, along *be* solid B. The arrow in the purely liquid region L shows the composition at which the cooling-curve 8.7 was taken.

The *overall* composition at any point in the diagram is always represented by the abscissa and the temperature by the ordinate. Thus, the point P in the area labelled 'L + S_B' stands for a system of known overall composition and temperature, which consists at equilibrium of a mixture of pure solid B and a liquid whose composition is found from the intersection of a horizontal line through P and the liquid composition line *be*.

Solubility and *depression of freezing-point* are much more closely related than might be supposed, and their connexion can be understood by reference to Figure 8.6. Consider a point in the liquid region to the left of the line be and at a temperature below b. Keeping the temperature fixed, imagine more B to be added continuously so that the point representing the overall composition moves to the right until eventually the line be is reached and no more B goes into solution. The composition at this point on be gives the solubility of the solute B in the solvent A at the chosen temperature. But if the point is near to b the same idea is expressed in different language: the point on be represents the depression of freezing-point of the solvent B by the solute A. (There is no profit in discussing whether sugar melts or dissolves in tea.)

§ 8.8 Quantitative expressions for the connexions between temperature and composition in a two-component system of condensed phases

Consider the quantitative aspects of the solubility lines ae and be. Provided that the solid phases are simply the crystals of the pure compounds (i.e. that solid solutions are not formed), their chemical potentials are only affected by the temperature. The chemical potentials in the liquid, on the other hand, are affected by both the temperature and the composition. To maintain equilibrium with respect to B along the line be therefore,

$$\begin{bmatrix} \text{Change in } {}^l\mu_B \text{ due to} \\ \text{change in composition} \end{bmatrix} + \begin{bmatrix} \text{Change in } {}^l\mu_B \text{ due} \\ \text{to change in } T \end{bmatrix}$$
$$= \begin{bmatrix} \text{Change in } {}^s\mu_B \text{ due} \\ \text{to change in } T \end{bmatrix}$$

The upper prefixes l and s stand for liquid and solid. Proceeding as in § 8.4,

$$\frac{\partial({}^l\mu_B/T)}{\partial \ln a_B} \, d \ln a_B + \frac{\partial({}^l\mu_B/T)}{\partial T} \, dT = \frac{\partial({}^s\mu_B/T)}{\partial T} \, dT \quad (8.8)$$

i.e. $$R \, d \ln a_B - \frac{{}^l h_B}{T^2} \, dT = - \frac{{}^s h_B}{T^2} \, dT$$

$$d \ln a_B = \frac{({}^l h_B - {}^s h_B)}{RT^2} \, dT \quad (8.9)$$

To integrate this exact relationship between the activity in the liquid phase and the solid–liquid equilibrium temperature, a knowledge of the temperature variation of the molar enthalpy change on melting, ${}^l h_B - {}^s h_B$, is required for the most accurate work, but as a very good first approximation this refinement can be ignored. If the partial molar enthalpy in the liquid is also independent of the composition (which is by no means always the case) the molar enthalpy change on melting is simply l_f, the latent heat of fusion of B, and the integrated form of (8.9) is

$$\ln a_B = - \frac{l_f}{R}\Big(\frac{1}{T} - \frac{1}{T_f}\Big) \quad (8.10)$$

The integration constant has been fixed by setting $a_B = 1$ (i.e. $\ln a_B = 0$) for pure B, for which the equilibrium temperature is, of course, the freezing-point, T_f.

For the special case of a perfect solution, which has $a_B = x_B$,

$$\ln x_B = - \frac{l_f}{R}\Big(\frac{1}{T} - \frac{1}{T_f}\Big) \quad (8.11)$$

Notice that the solubility of B expressed in mole-fraction terms is in this case determined only by its own heat of fusion and melting-point, and there is no specific reference to the other component at all except in so far as it affects the mole fraction. The solubility of a substance forming perfect solutions is therefore the same in all solvents.

(8.11) is sometimes known as the *perfect* or *ideal solubility equation*. The solubilities of some substances, such as naphthalene in certain organic solvents, can be calculated fairly well from it, but better approximations can usually be made with allowances for activity coefficients by the methods of § 7.7. Qualitatively, however, it expresses nicely the dependence of solubility on the melting-point and the heat of fusion: solubility is favoured by a low melting-point and a low heat of fusion, much as would be expected. Quantitatively it has a very important application in dilute solutions, where departures from ideality are less important. The simple connexion between the equilibrium temperature and the mole fraction, surprisingly independent of the nature of the other component, there becomes transformed into a freezing-point depression which depends only upon the number of moles of solute in a fixed weight of solvent and not upon the nature of the solute. The two approximations involved are:

(i) $\qquad \ln x_B = \ln(1 - x_A) \simeq -x_A \simeq -m_A/m_B = -m_2/m_1$

(with suffix 1 for solvent)

(ii) $\left(\dfrac{1}{T} - \dfrac{1}{T_f}\right) = (T_f - T)/TT_f \simeq \theta/T_f^2$

where θ is written for $T_f - T$, the depression of freezing-point. Substitution in (8.11) and rearrangement lead to

$$\theta = \left(\frac{RT_f^2}{m_1 l_f}\right)m_2 = k_f m_2 \qquad (8.12)$$

k_f is the *cryoscopic constant* of the solvent and is directly calculable from the molar heat of fusion, the freezing-point (in °K) and the number of moles of the solvent in a kilogram ($m_1 = 1,000/\text{m. Wt.}$). For most substances the entropies of fusion (l_f/T_f) are similar (though not so similar as the entropies of vaporization), so the cryoscopic constants tend to be roughly proportional to T_f and to have values about 5 deg mole^{-1} (kg solvent) at room temperature. But in certain cases some rotation sets in (with heat absorption) at a solid phase transition below the freezing-point, and less entropy is then gained on fusion, with the consequence that l_f is abnormally low and k_f abnormally high. Such solvents, e.g. camphor with $k_f = 40$ deg mole^{-1} (kg solvent) and cyclohexane with 20·2, have been especially useful in the determination of molecular weights in organic chemistry; for if the weight of solute per kilogram of solvent is known and the number of moles per kilogram is obtained experimentally from (8.12) the molecular weight can easily be calculated.

If a substance to which a molality m_2 is assigned simply on the basis of its formula weight actually gives rise to ν particles in solution it is easy to see from the way (8.12) was derived using the approximation (i) that θ will be given by $\nu k_f m_2$ instead of $k_f m_2$. In other words, the solvent mole fraction in (8.11) is affected by the total molality of solute particles, whatever their origin in terms of chemical formulae. For example, NaCl gives nearly twice and $CaCl_2$ nearly three times the molal depression of a non-electrolyte in water because of their complete dissociation into ions; and carboxylic acids produce only half the molar depressions expected in some organic solvents because of dimerization. Activity coefficients complicate the exact interpretation of the cryoscopic results for electrolytes in water, but these effects are less important in the solvent H_2SO_4, which freezes at $10 \cdot 37°C$ and provides very interesting chemical results because of its strongly acidic nature. In this solvent acetic acid behaves as a strong base (with $\nu = 2$), nitric acid gives rise to the important nitronium ion ($\nu = 4$) and triphenyl carbinol to a carbonium ion:

$$CH_3COOH + H_2SO_4 = CH_3C(OH)_2^+ + HSO_4^-$$
$$HNO_3 + 2H_2SO_4 = NO_2^+ + H_3O^+ + 2HSO_4^-$$
$$(C_6H_5)_3COH + 2H_2SO_4 = (C_6H_5)_3C^+ + H_3O^+ + 2HSO_4^-$$

Chemically interesting results often stand out in this way from the simplest treatment of cryoscopic results in terms of ideal behaviour, but the exact equation (8.9) also reveals the possibility of using freezing-point measurements for the determination of activity coefficients.

§ 8.9 Activity coefficients from solid–liquid equilibria

For a very dilute solution, replacement of T^2 by T_f^2 in (8.9) produces only a small error of the same order as that involved in neglecting the temperature variation of l_f. Thus to a close approximation l_f/RT^2 can be replaced by $1/m_1k_f$ and (8.9) by

$$\mathrm{d} \ln a_1 = -(1/m_1k_f)\mathrm{d}\theta \qquad (8.13)$$

As the equilibrium set up is between the solid and liquid phases of the solvent, it is naturally the *solvent* activity which is related to the freezing-point depression by this equation, which therefore can lead directly to the solvent osmotic coefficient. But changes in the activity of the *solute* are related to those of the solvent by the Gibbs–Duhem equation (6.13), in the activity form obtained by means of (2.15):

$$m_1\mathrm{d} \ln a_1 + m_2\mathrm{d} \ln a_2 = 0 \qquad (8.14)$$

Thus the solute activity in very dilute solutions satisfies the equation

$$\mathrm{d} \ln a_2 = (1/m_2k_f)\mathrm{d}\theta \qquad (8.15)$$

If the solute is an electrolyte, this can be expressed in terms of the mean activity, $a_{\pm}$ (i.e. $a_2^{1/\nu}$: see (7.32)):

$$\mathrm{d} \ln a_{\pm} = (1/\nu m_2k_f)\mathrm{d}\theta \qquad (8.16)$$

From (7.33) it follows that $m_{\pm}$ is proportional to m_2, whence $\mathrm{d} \ln m_{\pm}$ is the same as $\mathrm{d} \ln m_2$. So

$$\mathrm{d} \ln \gamma_{\pm} = \mathrm{d} \ln a_{\pm} - \mathrm{d} \ln m_{\pm} = (1/\nu m_2k_f)\mathrm{d}\theta - \mathrm{d} \ln m_2$$
$$= -\mathrm{d} \ln m_2 \left[1 - (\mathrm{d}\theta/\mathrm{d}m_2)(1/\nu k_f)\right] \qquad (8.17)$$

The integration of this equation looks troublesome, since $\ln m_2 \longrightarrow -\infty$ as $m_2 \longrightarrow 0$, but this effect is offset by the rapidly vanishing quantity in square brackets. A function $j = 1 - \theta/\nu m_2k_f$ is introduced to help in the final evaluation of $\gamma_{\pm}$ from the freezing-point data. (See Lewis and Randall, 1st edition, pp. 286–288, and 342–346.)

In concentrated solutions the variation of partial molar enthalpies with composition cannot be ignored. But a form similar to (8.10), with a term allowing for the temperature variation of l_f if necessary, can still be arrived at if the temperature change in (8.8) is regarded as carried out before the composition change. The temperature coefficients then refer to the pure liquid and solid but, since the composition change is carried out at the equilibrium temperature T, the activity must refer to this temperature and not to T_f. If all the activities are required at the same temperature, T_f, they have then to be corrected using the formula

$$\mathrm{d}\ln a_\mathrm{B}/\mathrm{d}T = -({}^l h_\mathrm{B} - {}^l h_\mathrm{B}{}^\circ)/RT^2 \qquad (8.18)$$
$$\text{(from (2.15) and (6.29))}$$

where $({}^l h_\mathrm{B} - {}^l h_\mathrm{B}{}^\circ)$ is the difference between the partial molar enthalpy of B in the actual solution and in the pure liquid.

§ 8.10 Equilibria involving sparingly soluble salts

At a fixed temperature and pressure a salt in a crystalline form has a fixed chemical potential. If it is to remain in equilibrium with a solution when composition changes are made its activity in the liquid phase must also remain constant. Thus the relevant condition for equilibrium is (see (7.32)):

$$a_2 = a_\pm{}^\nu = (m_+{}^{\nu+} m_-{}^{\nu-}) \times \gamma_\pm{}^\nu = K_\mathrm{s}. \qquad (8.19)$$

K_s is a constant at a fixed temperature and pressure and is known as the *solubility product*. It differs from the product $(m_+{}^{\nu+} m_-{}^{\nu-})$, which varies with the ionic strength, by the presence of the factor $\gamma_\pm{}^\nu$; but since even a sparingly soluble salt always makes some ionic strength contribution to the saturated solution, K_s can only be obtained by extrapolating the experimental $(m_+^{\nu^+} m_-^{\nu^-})$ product to zero ionic strength using a formula like (7.39) or (7.41).

Once K_s has been obtained for a given salt, solubility measurements can be used to investigate the effects of other salts upon the mean activity coefficient $\gamma_\pm$. For neutral salts,

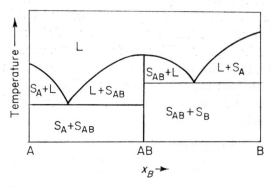

FIG. 8.8   Simple phase diagram for a two-component system with compound formation

with no ions in common with the solid phase, increase the solubility of a sparingly soluble salt appreciably by simply depressing $\gamma_\pm$ so that the molality product has to increase in (8.19).

§ 8.11 Solid–liquid equilibria with compound formation

Solid–liquid phase diagrams are usually much more complicated than Figure 8.6, even in two-component systems. Figure 8.8 shows the slightly more complicated diagram obtained when A and B form just one solid compound with the formula AB.

In many ways the new diagram resembles two figures like (8.6) joined together, but there is an interesting difference between AB and the two components A and B. As the composition of pure A (or B) is approached the solute concentration and activity diminish to zero and, by

$$\mu_i = \mu_i^\ominus + RT \ln a_i \qquad (2.15)$$

the solute chemical potential tends to $-\infty$. At AB, however, solutes are in a different situation: A and B can be both added to and subtracted from AB. This means that μ_A for the solute A in the solvent AB cannot be $-\infty$ at the composition AB, since it must be diminished still further by the removal of A. Generally this idea is made easier to grasp by the presence of free A and B at the actual composition AB due to some dissociation in the liquid state. It is then clear that their activities cannot be zero, but must increase continuously through this composition. Since $\partial\mu_A/\partial m_A$ is not infinite in the solvent AB at $m_A = 0$, it then follows from the Gibbs–Duhem equation (6.13) that $\partial\mu_{AB}/\partial m_A$ must be zero. This simply expresses the fact that the potential of the compound varies continuously with the composition and reaches a maximum at AB. The flatter the solid–liquid equilibrium curve is at this point, the greater is the extent of dissociation of the compound in the liquid state.

§ 8.12 Membrane equilibria

If two phases at a fixed temperature are separated by a membrane permeable to some molecular species but not to others, only the potentials of the species to which the membrane is permeable have to be considered in setting up the condition of equilibrium.

The simplest membrane equilibrium is the *osmotic equilibrium* between a pure solvent and a solution (see Fig. 8.9). The solute species dilute the solvent and so reduce its chemical potential in the solution phase, but equilibrium is preserved by applying pressure to this phase just sufficient to balance the dilution effect. The extra pressure is known as the *osmotic pressure* and is represented by π. It is calculated as follows:

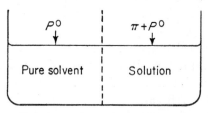

FIG. 8.9   Osmotic equilibrium

As the temperature is constant and the pure solvent remains open to the atmosphere, the solvent chemical potential must remain exactly the same throughout in both phases to preserve equilibrium. In the solution phase, therefore,

$$\begin{bmatrix} \text{Change in } \mu_1 \text{ due to} \\ \text{change in composition} \end{bmatrix} + \begin{bmatrix} \text{Change in } \mu_1 \text{ due to} \\ \text{change in pressure} \end{bmatrix} = 0$$

$$\int_0^{\ln a_1} \frac{\partial \mu_1}{\partial \ln a_1} \, d \ln a_1 + \int_{P^\circ}^{P^\circ + \pi} \frac{\partial \mu_1}{\partial P} \, dP = 0 \qquad (8.20)$$

$$\therefore \quad RT \ln a_1 + \int_{P^\circ}^{P^\circ + \pi} v_1 dP = 0 \qquad (8.21)$$

The (partial) molar volume of the solvent, v_1, is practically constant over ordinary pressure ranges and hardly affected by solutes in dilute solution, so

$$\pi v_1 = -RT \ln a_1 \qquad (8.22)$$

Solvent osmotic coefficients can be obtained directly from π with this formula, since $\ln a_1$ is $g_1 \ln x_1$. But for solutions dilute enough to be effectively ideal, $-\ln a_1 \simeq v m_2/m_1$ and $v_1 \simeq V/m_1$, and so

$$\pi V = v m_2 R T \qquad (8.23)$$

Since V/m_2 is the total volume containing a mole of the solute, this equation is analogous to the perfect gas equation.

At present (8.23) is most often used for the determination of the molecular weights of high polymers. In such systems deviations from ideality are appreciable even at low molalities (because of the large solute volume), and the molecular weight is therefore calculated from (8.23) at several concentrations, plotted against m_2 and extrapolated to $m_2 = 0$.

The *Donnan equilibrium* is another important type of membrane equilibrium, in which the membrane is permeable to small ions as well as to the solvent, but impermeable to large organic ions. If, for example, a solution of sodium chloride is on one side of the membrane and a solution of a chloride with a large organic cation on the other, sodium ions will be found on both sides of the membrane at equilibrium as the chemical potential of sodium chloride (i.e., $\mu_{Na+} + \mu_{Cl-}$) must become the same on both sides when the membrane is permeable to this salt.

Further work

Only a few of the very simplest types of phase equilibrium have been considered here. For an introduction to some of the possible complications see, e.g., W. J. Moore, *Physical Chemistry* (4th edition, Longmans, 1963), pp. 148–158 and 107–113.

Look at Gibbs, *Collected Works*, Vol. I, pp. 96–98 and 135–138.

Problems for Chapter 8

1. To justify the approximation $(^g v - {}^l v) \simeq {}^g v$ in the Clapeyron–Clausius equation, calculate the percentage error involved in neglecting the volume of the liquid phase of water at 0°C and 1 atm.

2. Given that the latent heat of fusion of ice is 80 cal g^{-1}

and the densities at $0°C$ of water and ice are $1·000$ and $0·917$ g cm^{-3} respectively, make an estimate of the temperature at the triple-point in the water–ice–vapour system using (8.4). (For this calculation the equilibrium vapour pressure at the triple-point can be regarded as negligible in comparison with 1 atm, which must in this case be converted into units compatible with those of $\Delta s/\Delta v$.) Also calculate k_f for water. (See (8.12).)

3. Examine the form of Bridgman's diagram for the phase equilibria of water at high pressures (Figure 25, p. 448, in *Z. anorg. Chem.*, 1912, **77**, 377). I shows the region of stability of ordinary ice and II, III, V and VI those of other forms of ice stable at high pressures: the top part of the diagram (unlabelled) is the region of stability of liquid water.

(*a*) From the forms of the solid–liquid equilibrium curves, deduce whether ice III, V and VI would float or sink.

(*b*) What are the chances of finding any of these solid forms at great depths in the sea? (Assume that the pressure increases by 1 atm for every 9 m of depth and that no point in the ocean is deeper than 9 km.)

4. Derive a formula similar to (8.12) for the elevation of the boiling-point of a solvent produced by an involatile solute of molality m_2.

5. Calcium iodate, $Ca(IO_3)_2$, dissolves to the extent of $7·84 \times 10^{-3}$ mole per litre at $25°C$.

(*a*) Estimate a value for K_s, using (7.41) to calculate $\gamma_{\pm}^3$. (See (7.34) and (8.19).)

(*b*) Estimate the percentage increase in solubility of this salt caused by the addition of $0·1 M$ NaCl.

6. The equilibrium water vapour pressures at $25°C$ over mixtures of hydrates of $CuSO_4$ having the analytical compositions $CuSO_4,0·6H_2O$, $CuSO_4,2H_2O$, and $CuSO_4,4·5H_2O$ were found to be $0·01$, $5·2$ and $7·8$ mm Hg respectively. Over a

solution saturated with the pentahydrate the vapour pressure was 23·1 mm Hg.

(*a*) Given that in the solid phase cupric sulphate is either anhydrous or has 1, 3 or 5 water molecules of hydration only, use these data to form a phase diagram, plotting equilibrium vapour pressure against the overall composition of the condensed phases present. (Pay particular attention to the degrees of freedom when 2 and 3 phases coexist at equilibrium in a two-component system at constant temperature.)

(*b*) How could osmotic coefficient tables for unsaturated solutions be used to extend the diagram?

(*c*) The equilibrium vapour pressure of the mixture of the anhydrous salt and the monohydrate is often quoted as 0·8 mm Hg, after the work of Foote and Scholes (*J. Amer. Chem. Soc.*, 1911, **33**, 1309, esp. p. 1324). Is this compatible with the results of Siggel in *Zeit. für Elektrochemie*, 1913, **19**, 340? (Look at the formula (12) at the end of the paper and the sample calculation for T = 273 just below.) Can you suggest a reason for rejecting the former result in this particular case?

9

Electromotive Force and the Free Energies of Ions in Solution

§ 9.1 Revision

When a Daniell cell is used to drive a current through an external circuit the reaction at the negative electrode supplies the electrons,

$$Zn\ (s) = Zn^{2+}\ (aq) + 2e^- \qquad (9.1)$$

and the reaction at the positive electrode absorbs them,

$$Cu^{2+}\ (aq) + 2e^- = Cu\ (s) \qquad (9.2)$$

The overall cell reaction, the free energy of which provides the electromotive force, is obtained by adding these two reactions together in such a way as to cancel out the electrons:

$$Zn\ (s) + Cu^{2+}\ (aq) = Zn^{2+}\ (aq) + Cu\ (s) \qquad (1.7)$$

In the construction of the cell the cupric ions have to be kept away from the zinc rod or this reaction would occur internally and the cell would run down. There has nevertheless to be a continuous electrical path, which is effected in the Daniell cell by having the solutions of zinc and cupric sulphates in contact, with interdiffusion minimized by a porous pot. (This

146

type of arrangement gives rise to a liquid junction potential which may amount to several millivolts and has to be allowed for, if it cannot be avoided, in accurate work.)

The e.m.f. is measured in volts (joules per coulomb) and the available work for the nF coulombs corresponding to the transport of n moles of electrons, according to some equation like (1.7), is nFE joules, i.e.

$$\Delta G = -nFE \qquad (1.9)$$

§ 9.2 Oxidation and reduction

Removal of electrons from a chemical species is *oxidation*; addition of electrons is *reduction*. (9.1) and (9.2) are both special cases of oxidation and reduction in which the reduced form, the metal, has a fixed chemical potential (and activity) at a given temperature and pressure. Cases in which both the oxidized and the reduced forms are of variable activity are also common:

$$Fe^{3+}(aq) + e^- = Fe^{2+}(aq) \qquad (9.3)$$
$$MnO_4^-(aq) + 8H^+(aq) + 5e^- = Mn^{2+}(aq) + 4H_2O(l) \qquad (9.4)$$

The electrons are then exchanged between the connecting wires and the system through a platinum electrode in contact with a mixture of the oxidized and reduced forms in solution.

In general, therefore, the driving force in a chemical cell is seen as arising from differences in the oxidizing and reducing power of the chemical species at the electrodes. Strong reducing agents, such as sodium, have a great tendency to give up electrons and so tend to form the negative pole of a cell, while strong oxidizing agents (permanganate) tend to form the positive pole. But polarity is a purely relative matter: if both electrode systems are ordinarily regarded as oxidizing, the stronger oxidizing agent gives the positive pole and the reduced form of the weaker is actually oxidized (i.e. has electrons abstracted from it) when the cell is working.

The following 'half-cell' reactions are arranged in order of oxidizing power, and in forming a complete cell from the electrode systems corresponding to any two of them, the higher on the list gives the positive pole and the lower the negative (for comparable concentrations of the species of variable activity):

TABLE 9.1

Half-cell reaction	$e^{\ominus}$ (volt) electrode potential with respect to solution (relative value only)
$Ce^4 + e^- = Ce^{3+}$	$+1 \cdot 61$
$MnO_4^- + 8H^+ + 5e^- = Mn^{2+} + 4H_2O$ (l)	$+1 \cdot 51$
$Ag^+ + e^- = Ag$ (s)	$+0 \cdot 7991$
$Fe^{3+} + e^- = Fe^{2+}$	$+0 \cdot 771$
$Cu^{2+} + 2e^- = Cu$ (s)	$+0 \cdot 337$
$H^+ + e^- = \frac{1}{2}H_2$ (g)	$0 \cdot 000$ (arbitrary zero)
$Zn^{2+} + 2e^- = Zn$ (s)	$-0 \cdot 763$
$Na^+ + e^- = Na$ (s)	$-2 \cdot 714$

The designation (aq) has been dropped for simplicity from all the ions in this table. (The last system cannot be used to form an electrode as it stands, because sodium metal reduces water to hydrogen. It has, however, been studied by the ingenious use of amalgams.) The hydrogen electrode is formed by bubbling gaseous hydrogen over a platinum foil in contact with an acid solution. To catalyse the reactions in the adsorbed layer so that the potential has its correct reversible value, the platinum has a coating of platinum black.

§ 9.3 Standard electrode potentials

At the right-hand side of Table 9.1 appear the standard electrode potentials, $e^{\ominus}$, which are measures of oxidizing power relative to the hydrogen ion when all species are in their standard states at unit activity. Fixing the scale by setting the zero by the hydrogen reaction is quite arbitrary but very convenient and universally adopted.

The standard e.m.f., $E^\ominus$, of any cell (i.e. the value of E when all the reactants are at unit activity) is now obtainable from the difference between the two relevant $e^\ominus$ values. From a table like 9.1, therefore, we can deduce the cell polarity, its $E^\ominus$ and its corresponding chemical reaction.

For example, the cell formed from a platinum electrode dipping into a mixture of ferric and ferrous salts and a copper rod dipping into a solution of a cupric salt is represented schematically as

$$\text{Cu (s)} \mid \text{Cu}^{2+} \text{(aq)} \parallel \text{Fe}^{3+} \text{(aq), Fe}^{2+} \text{(aq)} \mid \text{Pt} \quad (9.5)$$

with the positive electrode on the right. (The copper is negative here, although positive to zinc.) The standard e.m.f. is $0.771 - 0.337 = 0.434$ volt, and the standard free energy of the corresponding reaction is $-0.434F$, i.e. -41.9 kjoule (-10 kcal) if the cell reaction is written as

$$\text{Fe}^{3+} + \tfrac{1}{2}\text{Cu (s)} = \text{Fe}^{2+} + \tfrac{1}{2}\text{Cu}^{2+} \quad (9.6)$$

or -20 kcal if the cell reaction is written as

$$2\text{Fe}^{3+} + \text{Cu (s)} = 2\text{Fe}^{2+} + \text{Cu}^{2+} \quad (9.7)$$

The half-cell reactions, as written in the table, are electron-consuming reactions and so indicate the spontaneous direction at the positive pole. When the change at the negative electrode is required the reaction has, of course, to be reversed; and the overall cell reaction is then obtained by addition of the spontaneous processes at both electrodes, suitably scaled so that the electrons cancel. The number of electrons cancelled is the n required in the formula nFE.

Because hydrogen is chosen as the zero for the scale, some of the standard potentials are negative, and this has to be remembered when finding $E^\ominus$ for cells involving these potentials. Copper and zinc are $1 \cdot 100$ volt apart on the scale, for example, and this is arrived at by remembering the sign of $e^\ominus_{Zn}$ when using the simple equation connecting the potentials of the positive and negative electrodes, e_+ and e_-, with the cell e.m.f. E:

$$E = e_+ - e_- \tag{9.8}$$
$$E^\ominus = e^\ominus_{Cu} - e^\ominus_{Zn} = +0 \cdot 337 - (-0 \cdot 763)$$
$$= 1 \cdot 100 \text{ volt} \tag{9.9}$$

§ 9.4 The standard free energies of formation of ions

Once having accepted the convention that reactions involving the gain or loss of electrons are to be measured *relative to the oxidizing power of the hydrogen ion*, we can treat the half-cell reactions in Table 9.1 formally just like other reactions. Thus $e^\ominus$ values are related to the conventional standard free energies of these reactions by the usual formula, $-nFe^\ominus$. Thermodynamic terms for the electrons can, however, be eliminated by setting the standard free energy of formation of the hydrogen ion (at unit activity) at zero, since half-cell reactions like (9.2) are really convenient shortened forms of reactions like

$$Cu^{2+} \text{ (aq)} + H_2 \text{ (g)} = Cu \text{ (s)} + 2H^+ \text{ (aq)} \quad (9.10)$$

with the hydrogen ions at unit activity and the hydrogen gas at unit pressure. Now the metals in such equations are in their standard states of zero free energy of formation, and so are the hydrogen species. As the standard free energies of these reactions are obtainable from the standard electrode potentials, the free energies of formation of the only remaining species, the metal ions, can therefore be found.

Notice particularly, however, that the standard potential reactions have the metal ions on the left-hand side and so represent the reverse process to the formation of the (positive) ions. While $-nFe^\ominus$ gives the free energy change correctly for reactions like (9.2) or (9.10) therefore, the sign has to be changed again to get to the standard free energy of formation of the metal ion, which thus has the same sign as the standard potential. This makes sense, since metals with negative standard potentials, like zinc, tend to form ions spontaneously relative to hydrogen (displace it from acid solution), and this process must therefore be accompanied by a decrease in the free energy (negative ΔG).

Once the free energies of some ions have been determined directly in this way, those of others can be obtained by the usual step-wise procedure using other oxidation–reduction potentials (for systems like Fe^{3+}/Fe^{2+}) or other equilibria. For example, it is only necessary to know the free energy of formation of water and the ionic product to calculate the standard free energy of formation of the hydroxyl ion.

Up to this point it has been convenient to follow the rule that a cell scheme like (9.5) should be written down with the positive electrode on the right, but a more general rule is useful in certain applications. If hypothetical cells are considered in a schematic way, for example, and not actually constructed in the laboratory it may not be obvious which *is* the positive electrode. The rule is then to proceed as if the right-hand electrode were positive and to allow the final sign of the overall e.m.f. to turn out negative if the cell chosen corresponds to a cell reaction going against the natural direction: i.e. *always calculate E as $e_{\text{right}} - e_{\text{left}}$ and write the half-cell reaction for the right-hand electrode in the usual way, with electrons on the left.*

For example, each $e^{\ominus}$ value of Table 9.1. can be regarded as the standard e.m.f. of a cell having the hydrogen electrode as reference on the left (with its half-cell reaction reversed) and the electrode of interest on the right (with its half-cell reaction as in the table). The overall reaction then appears in each case with the hydrogen species as in (9.10), but represents a spontaneous reaction or otherwise according to whether the sign of the e.m.f. is positive or negative.

§ 9.5 The effect of concentration on e.m.f.

Any cell reaction, such as (1.7), (9.7), (9.10), can be represented in the general terms of Chapter 1:

$$\nu_A A + \nu_B B + \ldots = \nu_C C + \nu_D D + \ldots \quad (1.1)$$

The free energy change is then

$$\Delta G = \nu_C \mu_C + \nu_D \mu_D \ldots - \nu_A \mu_A - \nu_B \mu_B \ldots$$

or, after expressing all the μ_i as $\mu_i^{\ominus} + RT \ln a_i$ and collecting the $\mu^{\ominus}$ terms together as $\Delta G^{\ominus}$ in the usual way,

$$\Delta G = \Delta G^{\ominus} + RT \ln \frac{(C)^{\nu_C}(D)^{\nu_D} \ldots}{(A)^{\nu_A}(B)^{\nu_B} \ldots} \quad (9.11)$$

The round brackets, ( ), stand for activities as before.

The activities occur in (9.11) as in an equilibrium constant, but are not in general equilibrium values. (When they *are* equilibrium values, $E = 0$, $\Delta G = 0$ and (9.11) reduces to the reaction isotherm.)

When E is substituted for $-\Delta G/nF$ and $E^{\ominus}$ for $-\Delta G^{\ominus}/nF$ (9.11) becomes

$$E = E^{\ominus} + \frac{RT}{nF} \ln \frac{(A)^{\nu_A}(B)^{\nu_B} \ldots}{(C)^{\nu_C}(D)^{\nu_D} \ldots} \quad (9.12)$$

The activity quotient has been inverted to annul the minus sign before the logarithmic term, and so occurs the other way up from an equilibrium constant. E is a measure of the driving force of the reaction and this will, of course, be increased by increasing the activities of the reactants, just as required by (9.12). In practice, the form of the logarithmic term is often simpler than this general formula indicates, because certain constituents, such as pure metals or a solvent in large excess, remain at unit activity throughout.

As an example, consider the cell for which the spontaneous reaction is (9.10). This has a positive copper electrode immersed in a cupric solution and a negative hydrogen electrode immersed in an acid. According to (9.12),

$$E = E^{\ominus} + \frac{RT}{2F} \ln \left(\frac{(Cu^{2+})P_{H_2}}{(H^+)^2} \right) \qquad (9.13)$$

Copper metal is at unit activity, and the activity of hydrogen gas has been expressed in terms of its pressure in atmospheres (i.e. the formula $\mu^{\circ} + RT \ln p$ has been used instead of $\mu^{\ominus} + RT \ln a$ for this species and the standard state is the gas at unit pressure). When the species H_2 and H^+ are in their standard states so that (9.10) is equivalent to (9.2), (9.13) reduces to

$$e_{Cu} = e^{\ominus}{}_{Cu} + \frac{RT}{2F} \ln (Cu^{2+}) \qquad (9.14)$$

which shows how the copper electrode potential varies with the concentration of the cupric ion. (The positive sign in (9.14) is expected, since increasing the concentration increases the rate of deposition of positive ions on the electrode in the dynamic equilibrium which exists at the surface.)

Equations like (9.14) can be set up formally for any of the half-cell reactions in Table 9.1; e.g.

$$e_{Ag} = e^{\ominus}{}_{Ag} + \frac{RT}{F} \ln (Ag^+) \qquad (9.15)$$

$$e_{Fe^{3/2}} = e^{\ominus}{}_{Fe^{3/2}} + \frac{RT}{F} \ln \frac{(Fe^{3+})}{(Fe^{2+})} \qquad (9.16)$$

$$e_{Mn^{7/2}} = e^{\ominus}{}_{Mn^{7/2}} + \frac{RT}{5F} \ln \frac{(MnO_4^-)(H^+)^8}{(Mn^{2+})} \qquad (9.17)$$

At $25°C$ $(RT/F) \ln x$ is equivalent to $0.059 \log_{10} x$ (volt), and so the copper electrode potential changes by about 30 mV when the cupric ion activity changes by a factor of ten. The silver electrode potential, on the other hand, changes by about 60 mV for a tenfold change in the silver ion activity. This rather small dependence of electrode potentials on activities is very important for potentiometric titrations in analysis. If ferrous iron is titrated with permanganate in acid solution, for example, up to very near the end-point the concentrations of ferrous and ferric ions are of the same order of magnitude, and the potential therefore remains in the region of $+0\cdot77$ volt. (See Table 9.1 and equation (9.16).) But since $e^{\ominus}$ for the manganese ion system is at $+1\cdot51$ volt, it follows from (9.17) that the ratio of permanganate to manganous ion must then be extremely small. When, however, the end-point is passed the position is reversed: the two manganese ions become comparable in concentration, the potential rises to about $1\cdot5$ volts and the ferrous ion has for practical purposes completely disappeared from the system. Near the end-point the rate of change of potential with the volume of permanganate solution added is very large and easily detectable on a simple potentiometer. Experimentally the potential is picked up by a platinum electrode dipping into the solution, and the cell is usually completed by a compact form of calomel (or silver–silver chloride) half-cell kept at a constant potential.

Exactly the same principle applies to the titration of an acid with a base, using a hydrogen electrode to respond to the hydrogen-ion concentration:

$$e_H = e^{\ominus}_H + 0\cdot059 \log_{10} (H^+) \simeq e^{\ominus}_H - 0\cdot059 \, pH \quad (9.18)$$

If the solutions are $0\cdot1M$ the pH begins in the region of 1 and changes by 2 units, thus changing the potential by only $0\cdot12$ volt, when 99% of the acid has been neutralized. But 1% excess of a strong base takes the pH immediately to 11, and this rapid change of 8 pH units produces a change of nearly half a volt. In practice, a calomel half-cell is often used as a reference in potentiometric pH titrations also, but the pH-sensitive electrode is not usually the hydrogen electrode itself but a glass electrode, which responds to pH in the same quantitative way (9.18).

154

§ 9.6 pH and oxidation–reduction couples in acidic and basic solutions

It has already been emphasized that the activity coefficients of single ions, though very convenient in a formal way for expressing ionic equilibria, are not separately determinable: only combinations of them can be measured. A single ionic activity appearing in some convenient equation like (9.14), being the product of an ionic activity coefficient and a molality, is therefore not experimentally accessible; but it will always appear, when the cell is completed, compounded with some other activity coefficient or combination of activity coefficients.

While there is consequently no well-defined meaning, strictly speaking, to the identification of pH with $- \log_{10} a_{H^+}$ expressed in (9.18), it is both convenient and permissible to think of pH in this way for practical purposes. Originally pH was defined as $-\log_{10} c_{H^+}$, but it is now given an 'operational' definition in terms of the e.m.f. of a specially constructed cell designed to measure logarithmically the changes in the product of the hydrogen-ion concentration and a mean activity coefficient formally similar to that of a singly charged ion. Once the pH values of certain buffers have been determined in this standard cell, which incorporates a hydrogen electrode, they can be used to calibrate the ordinary laboratory pH measuring devices.

The electrode potentials of systems like (9.4) involving H^+ are sensitive to pH (see (9.17)) and so are quoted in tables for unit activity of hydrogen ion (zero pH). Sometimes such systems are also of interest in alkaline solutions and may then be quoted also for unit activity of hydroxide ion (pH 14). But from the additivity of free energy equations, it follows that these potentials in acidic and basic solutions are simply connected by the ionic product of water. For example, the reduction of oxygen in acid solution is represented by the half-cell equations

$$O_2 \text{ (g)} + 4H^+ \text{ (aq)} + 4e^- = 2H_2O \text{ (l)} \qquad (9.19)$$

$$e = 1.229 + \frac{RT}{4F} \ln p_{O_2} (H^+)^4 \qquad (9.20)$$

In alkaline solution the (H^+) can be replaced by $K_w/(OH^-)$, where K_w is the ionic product of water and (9.20) is transformed into

$$e = \left[1.229 + \frac{RT}{F} \ln K_w \right] + \frac{RT}{4F} \ln p_{O_2}/(OH^-)^4 \qquad (9.21)$$

which corresponds to the half-cell reaction

$$O_2 \text{ (g)} + 2H_2O \text{ (l)} + 4e^- = 4OH^- \text{ (aq)} \qquad (9.22)$$

At 25 °C the extra factor involving K_w brings the standard potential for the reduction of oxygen down to 0·401 volt. (What value of K_w has been assumed?) In pure water, with a pH of 7, the corresponding potential is exactly halfway between these two numbers, 0·815 volt.

If it were not for the fact that the oxidation of water to oxygen proceeds very slowly in the absence of a catalyst, oxidizing agents like permanganate and ceric, with standard potentials greater than 1·23 volt, would be spontaneously reduced in aqueous solution and quite unavailable as analytical reagents. But the phenomenon of 'overvoltage', attributable to the presence of high energies of activation in certain of the stages of the reactions, gives these substances an extra lease of life by putting the potential at which water is oxidized at all rapidly up by about 0·5 volt.

A similar phenomenon occurs in the reduction of the hydrogen ion to hydrogen gas, which also only occurs at all rapidly in the absence of a catalyst at a potential of about 0·5 volt more negative than the equilibrium value. The standard potential of this system in acid solution is, of course, zero, but the actual reversible potential for hydrogen evolution shifts by 59 mV for every unit of pH until it stands at 0·828 volt at pH 14. Any couple more negative than this potential at a given pH is therefore thermodynamically unstable: any reducing agent with a more negative potential which remains unchanged in aqueous solution does so by virtue of 'overvoltage'. The 0·5 volt extension to the range is only a rough guide, and the real potential at which reduction of the hydrogen ions becomes serious depends on the nature of the system. Chromous chloride will liberate hydrogen from dilute hydrochloric acid, for example ($e^{\ominus}$ for $Cr^{3+}/Cr^{2+} = -0\cdot41$ volt), whereas, on the other hand, some metals with electrode potentials considerably more negative than hydrogen are deposited electrolytically in preference to hydrogen in industrial processes, and this is rendered possible by overvoltage.

Half-cell reactions like (9.4) are set up as follows:

1. The valence state of the reducible atom in the oxidized and reduced forms must first be decided. (For the permanganate system the reduced form in acid solution is known to be Mn^{2+} and the oxidized form has Mn in the $7+$ state, since the four oxygens are all bound directly to the Mn atom and contribute -2 each to the ionic charge of MnO_4^{-}.)

2. The number of electrons required is then given by the difference in the valence states of the oxidized and the reduced forms, and the equation is set out with the oxidized form plus electrons on the left and the reduced form on the right.

3. The oxygens from ions like MnO_4^{-} are then either balanced out with hydrogen ions to form water, if the equation is required for acid solutions, or combined with water to form hydroxide ions (see (9.22)) if the solution is alkaline.

§ 9.7 Electrodes reversible to negative ions

So far, only electrodes reversible to positive ions have been considered. The effect of the ionic activity on an electrode reversible to a negative ion differs from (9.14) by having a negative sign before the logarithmic term, since increasing the negative ion concentration makes the electrode more negative.

Although electrodes similar to the hydrogen electrode can be constructed for the halogens, with half-cell reactions like

$$\tfrac{1}{2}Cl_2 \text{ (g)} + e^- = Cl^- \text{ (aq)} \qquad (9.23)$$

they are not much used because the same function is discharged more conveniently by electrodes reversible to positive ions in the presence of sparingly soluble salts. The conversion of the usual expression for a positive ion to that for a negative ion is then exactly the same in principle as the change from (9.20) to (9.21). In that case (H^+) was replaced by $K_w/(OH^-)$; but in a very similar way (Ag^+) in the equation for the silver electrode potential can be replaced by $K_s/(Cl^-)$ if solid silver chloride is present in the system (K_s being the solubility product of silver chloride).

$$e_{Ag} = e^{\ominus}{}_{Ag} + \frac{RT}{F} \ln \, (Ag^+)$$

$$= \left(e^{\ominus}{}_{Ag} + \frac{RT}{F} \ln K_s \right) - \frac{RT}{F} \ln \, (Cl^-)$$

$$= e^{\ominus}{}_{AgCl/Ag} - \frac{RT}{F} \ln \, (Cl^-) \qquad (9.24)$$

Clearly, if $e^{\ominus}{}_{Ag}$ and $e^{\ominus}{}_{AgCl/Ag}$ can be measured accurately, the difference between the two determines K_s. Several sparingly soluble salts have been investigated in this way, but the silver chloride and mercurous chloride systems are especially important, as they are widely used in reference electrodes.

To maintain proper equilibrium between the metal electrode, the solid salt and the solution, it is necessary in accurate work to deposit the salt on the surface of the metal. In the case of the silver system, a paste of silver oxide is usually baked on to a platinum rod to produce finely divided silver, and the chloride is then deposited electrolytically.

§ 9.8 Activity coefficients from e.m.f. measurements

When a silver–silver chloride and a hydrogen electrode dip into a hydrochloric acid solution, the silver electrode is found to have positive polarity, and so the e.m.f. of the cell can be expressed as follows:

$$E = \left\{ e^{\ominus}{}_{AgCl/Ag} - \frac{RT}{F} \ln (Cl^-) \right\} - \left\{ e^{\ominus}{}_H + \frac{RT}{F} \ln (H^+) \right\}$$

$$= E^{\ominus} - \frac{RT}{F} \ln (H^+)(Cl^-)$$

$$= E^{\ominus} - \frac{RT}{F} \ln [H^+][Cl^-] (\gamma_{H^+}\gamma_{Cl^-})$$

$$= E^{\ominus} - \frac{2RT}{F} \ln m - \frac{2RT}{F} \ln \gamma_+. \tag{9.25}$$

(Square brackets, [ ], stand for molalities and round brackets, ( ), for activities.)

In this equation $E^{\ominus}$ for the whole cell is equivalent to the half-cell $e^{\ominus}{}_{AgCl/Ag}$ relative to hydrogen, and the factor of 2 has appeared before the logarithmic terms because, on the one hand, $[H^+] = [Cl^-] = m$, the molality of the HCl, and, on the other $\gamma_{H^+}\gamma_{Cl^-} = \gamma_{\pm}^2$, the square of the mean activity coefficient, by (7.34). Once $E^{\ominus}$ has been determined, therefore, $\gamma_{\pm}$ can be evaluated at all concentrations from the e.m.f. measurements by (9.25).

To get $E^{\ominus}$, the quantity $\left[E + \frac{2RT}{F} \ln m \right]$ can be plotted against $m^{\frac{1}{2}}$ and extrapolated to zero concentration, since in this way the scale is fixed by setting $\gamma_{\pm} = 1$ at infinite dilution, and a good linear extrapolation is expected because of the known dependence of $\ln \gamma_{\pm}$ on $m^{\frac{1}{2}}$ at extreme dilutions. (A better extrapolation still is made by incorporating the theoretical $m^{\frac{1}{2}}$ dependence into the ordinates and plotting against m.)

§ 9.9 The standard entropies of ions

The standard entropy changes of many reactions involving ions are obtained directly from the variation of $E^{\ominus}$ with temperature:

$$\Delta S^{\ominus} = -\frac{\partial \Delta G^{\ominus}}{\partial T} = nF \frac{\partial E^{\ominus}}{\partial T} \qquad (6.25)$$

But the entropy change of the reaction is simply the difference between the product and reactant entropies (4.14); e.g. for reaction (9.10).

$$\Delta S^{\ominus} = s^{\circ}_{Cu} + 2s^{\ominus}_{H^+} - s^{\ominus}_{Cu^{2+}} - s^{\circ}_{H_2} \qquad (9.26)$$

The standard entropies of the elements are known (from specific heat measurements, § 5.6), and so the cell measurements allow the difference $2s^{\circ}_{H^+} - s^{\ominus}_{Cu^{2+}}$ to be evaluated.

The next step is to adopt the (arbitrary) convention that $e^{\ominus}$ for the hydrogen electrode is zero at all temperatures, whence not only $e^{\ominus}_{298}$ (say) but also $\partial e^{\ominus}/\partial T$ is zero. This makes $s^{\ominus}_{H^+}$ zero and the difference $2s^{\ominus}_{H^+} - s^{\ominus}_{Cu^{2+}}$ conventionally equal to $-s^{\ominus}_{Cu^{2+}}$. Hence entropy values can be tabulated for single ions.

Because of their charges, ions cause considerable disturbances in the orientation of polar solvent molecules in their vicinity, with the result that entropy is an important factor in determining the position of equilibrium in ionic reactions. This is particularly true of reactions involving changes in the number of ions, as in the dissociation of acetic acid, which is accompanied by a large entropy decrease because of the ordering effect of the ions on the solvent. (Cf. problem 4.3.)

§ 9.10 Variation of e.m.f. with temperature

This experiment can be set up easily in the laboratory.

The e.m.f. of the cell $Pt, H_2 \mid HCl(0 \cdot 1M) \mid AgCl, Ag$ is measured with the galvanometer connected such that the pointer moves to the right if the e.m.f. of the cell increases (see Figure 9.1).

Remembering that the cell reaction is

$$H_2 \text{ (g)} + 2AgCl \text{ (s)} = 2H^+ \text{ (aq)} + 2Cl^- \text{ (aq)} + 2Ag \text{ (s)},$$

and that $dE/dT = \Delta S/nF$, guess which way the pointer will move finally if the hot plate is switched on for a time and the

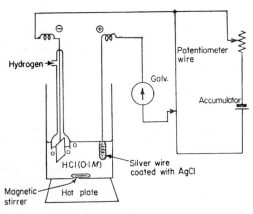

FIG. 9.1   The variation of e.m.f. with temperature

cell allowed to equilibrate at a higher temperature. (See problems 4.3 and 5.6 and § 9.9.)

Confirm your guess by finding $\Delta S^{\ominus}$ from tables.

Further work

Warning

Many of the older text-books and papers adopt the opposite sign convention for standard electrode potentials. This involves changing not only the signs of all $e^{\ominus}$ values but also the signs before the logarithmic terms in half-cell potentials (to preserve the same magnitudes): the equations for half-cell reactions are also reversed and have the electrons on the right. (Perhaps the easiest way to see which convention is adopted is to look at the signs of the alkali metals and the oxidizing agents in the $e^\ominus$ table.) Unfortunately the best compilation of electrode potential data (Latimer) adopts this convention, which is the opposite of the internationally recommended convention used in this chapter.

Read Latimer's *Oxidation Potentials*, 2nd ed., pp. 38–43, 127–134.

Useful accounts of related topics are given in the Royal Institute of Chemistry Monographs for Teachers. (See especially No. 1 by C. W. Davies and No. 2 by A. G. Sharpe.)

For the further study of liquid junction potentials see D. A. MacInnes, *Principles of Electrochemistry* (Reinhold, 1939), Chapter 13, and D. H. Everett, *An Introduction to the Study of Chemical Thermodynamics* (Longmans, London, 1959), pp. 132–139.

A good source of information on the construction of electrodes is *Reference Electrodes*, Ed. by D. J. G. Ives and G. J. Janz, Academic Press, 1961.

For the molecular theory of ionic processes see R. W. Gurney, *Ionic Processes in Solution*, McGraw-Hill, 1953.

Problems for Chapter 9

1. What value of the ionic product of water is consistent with the standard free energy of OH⁻ (aq) in Latimer's Table (2nd ed., p. 39)?

2. Sketch a potentiometric curve (electrode potential against ml added) for the titration of a ferrous sulphate solution with ceric sulphate.

3. Hydrogen bubbles over a platinum electrode in a labora-

tory in which the pressure is 750 mm Hg, while the vapour pressure of water over the solution is 20 mm Hg. What correction must be applied (at 25°C) to the hydrogen electrode potential in the cell to find the value at standard pressure?

4. (*a*) In a cell formed from a reference half-cell of fixed potential and a mercury electrode in contact with a solution of mercurous perchlorate, it is found that a tenfold dilution of the mercurous salt changes the e.m.f. by about 30 mV.

Deduce a formula for the mercurous ion.

(*b*) The standard potential of the mercurous–mercury system is +0·789 volt, and that of the calomel–mercury-chloride system +0·268 volt. Calculate the solubility product of calomel (mercurous chloride).

5. Set up half-cell reactions for the following:

(*a*) The reduction of iodate to I_2 in dilute acid solution.

(*b*) The reduction of iodate to I^+ (as I Cl) in concentrated hydrochloric acid solution.

(*c*) The reduction of ortho-arsenic acid to meta-arsenious acid (both undissociated) in acid solution.

(*d*) The reduction of permanganate to manganese dioxide in basic solution.

Assign to each reaction an $e^\ominus$ value, either by finding the appropriate value in Latimer's Tables 84 and 85 (and changing the sign) or by indirect methods from free energy data where the $e^\ominus$ values are not listed.

10

Thermodynamics and Kinetics

§ 10.1 The laws of thermodynamics

Thermodynamic arguments are characterized by predictions of the possible behaviour of a system in certain conditions from a knowledge of the way it actually behaves in some other, often apparently unrelated, conditions. The underlying idea is one of *consistency*: the occurrence of the forbidden behaviour would entail other special properties of the system which would be found to be inconsistent with those already known. There must surely still be room for progress in the examination of this notion of consistency, but historically it has been found satisfactory to erect the structure of thermodynamics on three laws which appear to be independent and serve as the axioms from which the theorems of thermodynamics are deduced.

The first law

Energy can neither be created nor destroyed but only changed from one form to another. (For large energy changes, as in nuclear processes, mass has to be regarded as a form of energy to preserve this conservation law.)

This idea appears in § 3.2 in the form that the change in the total energy of a system is equal to the heat it absorbs less the work it does. If no heat is exchanged with the surroundings and no work is done, whatever else may happen inside a system, its total energy remains constant. If the temperature then rises, you have to say that the increase in thermal energy is compensated by a negative ΔU characteristic of the chemical change taking place.

The second law

In any natural (spontaneous) change there is always an overall increase in entropy.

As stated in § 5.8, it is always possible to define the limits of a system in such a way that it is large enough to contain all the changes which take place; and then, according to the first law, such a system cannot change in energy and the drift towards the highest entropy is sufficient to determine the direction of natural changes.

The third law

The absolute zero of temperature is unattainable.

It can be shown to follow from this that there can be no entropy change in reactions between perfectly crystalline substances at $0°K$, and hence that the numerical values of the entropies of such substances can conveniently be set at zero at $0°K$, as assumed in § 5.4. (See Fowler and Guggenheim, *Statistical Thermodynamics*, Cambridge, 1949, pp. 224–226.)

These statements of the laws are chosen to give a simple indication of their content and are not necessarily the most acceptable forms logically. Even the first law, which often looks fairly straightforward to beginners, involves some subtlety in the precise definition of heat and work and may look different when provision is made for this. (See Guggenheim, *Thermodynamics*, North-Holland, 2nd ed., 1950, p. 7.) For a precise demonstration of the equivalence of the various historical statements of the *second* law see Kirkwood and Oppenheim, *Chemical Thermodynamics*, McGraw-Hill, 1961, Chapter 4.

For many chemists, however, the outstanding problem in

M

regard to the second law is how to reconcile the universal increase in entropy with the fact that it is the ΔG and not the ΔS characteristic of a chemical process which determines the direction of change at constant temperature and pressure. This problem was dealt with in Chapter 5, where it was explained that the ΔS for the process itself is not the whole of the entropy change which occurs if the process happens to be accompanied by the interchange of heat with the surroundings. When the entropy change in the surroundings is also taken into account $-\Delta G/T$ emerges as the overall increase in entropy accompanying the unharnessed reaction, and hence gives the tendency for the change to take place. Thus the ΔS of a spontaneous chemical process can even be negative, provided that sufficient heat is expelled to produce a greater positive ΔS outside.

Once properly understood, the equation $\Delta G = \Delta H - T\Delta S$ therefore nicely summarizes the roles of energy and entropy in chemistry. When the system is left to itself in thermal contact with its surroundings the energy is simply redistributed among the molecules inside and outside the system until the most probable arrangement is arrived at. The internal entropy change is then determined only by the initial and final states inside, while the characteristic internal energy change comes into the assessment of the entropy change in the surroundings.

§ 10.2 Direct application of the entropy law

Many useful formulae have been derived in the preceding chapters from the point of view of chemical potentials, because of their widespread occurrence in the chemical literature and their direct relationship to elementary ideas about potential and work. Further insight can, however, be gained by the direct application of the entropy criterion: for a process carried out at equilibrium there must be no overall change in entropy, i.e. internal and external entropy changes must cancel one another. (See end of Chapter 5.)

Figure 10.1 illustrates two examples of the derivation of important formulae by this alternative method. In both cases the external entropy decrease is due to absorption of latent heat by the system, and, since this entropy loss $(-l/T)$ has to be balanced by the internal entropy gain, the latter must equal l/T at equilibrium. The presentation has been simplified by the omission of slight correction terms, which are easily incorporated if required. (In this latter respect, notice that if you retain the correction for the temperature variation of the standard entropies, $\int \Delta C_p \mathrm{d} \ln T$, you must also retain that for the temperature variation of the latent heat, $\Delta C_p (T_2 - T_1)$, as these corrections are similar in magnitude and practically cancel.)

As a further example of this alternative method, consider the shift of chemical equilibrium with temperature in a perfect solution. The internal entropy increase for the amount of chemical change represented by the equation

$$\nu_A A + \nu_B B + \ldots = \nu_C C + \nu_D D + \ldots \quad (1.1)$$

is $\quad \Delta S = \nu_C s_C + \nu_D s_D + \ldots - \nu_A s_A - \nu_B s_B - \ldots$

But since all the s_i can be written as $s_i^\circ - R \ln x_i$ for a perfect solution (as deduced from first principles in § 7.3),

$$\Delta S = \Delta S^\circ - R \ln \left(x_C^{\nu_C} x_D^{\nu_D} \ldots / x_A^{\nu_A} x_B^{\nu_B} \ldots \right)$$

i.e. $\quad \Delta S = \Delta S^\circ - R \ln K \quad\quad\quad (10.1)$

if all the x_i refer to equilibrium conditions, K being the equilibrium constant.

At equilibrium, this entropy increase is balanced by the decrease in entropy in the thermostat, which supplies the heat of reaction, ΔH (and this, in a perfect system, is the same as ΔH°, the enthalpy change when the species are in their standard states). Hence

$$\Delta H^\circ / T = \Delta S^\circ - R \ln K \quad\quad\quad (10.2)$$

which is equivalent to $\Delta G^\circ = -RT \ln K$.

FIG. 10.1 Alternative derivations of (8.6) and (8.11). (Simplified by omission of small correction terms to concentrate on essential features.)

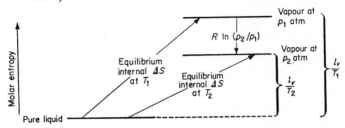

(a) *Dependence of vapour pressure upon temperature:* for the isothermal expansion of a mole of gas from v_1 to v_2 the entropy increase is $k \ln (v_2/v_1)^{N_0} = R \ln (v_2/v_1) = -R \ln (p_2/p_1)$.

The diagram illustrates directly the relationship

$$R \ln \left(\frac{p_2}{p_1}\right) = l_v \left(\frac{1}{T_1} - \frac{1}{T_2}\right).$$

Starting from the pure liquid at the bottom of the diagram, there is a greater entropy increase on evaporation to the lower v.p. at the lower temperature, and this is balanced by dividing the latent heat by the smaller temperature value.

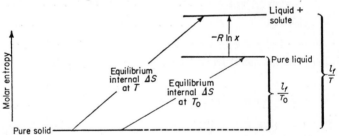

(b) *Dependence of solubility upon temperature in a perfect solution:* formula (7.8) is used for the effect of dilution upon the liquid entropy. (x is the mole fraction of the component having the solid form present.)

The diagram illustrates directly the relationship

$$-R \ln x = l_f \left(\frac{1}{T} - \frac{1}{T_0}\right).$$

Starting from the pure solid at the bottom of the diagram, there is a greater entropy increase on dissolving to form the diluted liquid at the lower temperature, and this is balanced by dividing the latent heat by the smaller temperature value.

By differentiation with respect to temperature (at constant pressure),

$$-\frac{\Delta H^\circ}{T^2} + \frac{1}{T}\frac{\partial \Delta H^\circ}{\partial T} = \frac{\partial \Delta S^\circ}{\partial T} - R\frac{\partial \ln K}{\partial T}$$

But since $\partial \Delta H^\circ / \partial T = \Delta C_p^\circ$ and $\partial \Delta S^\circ / \partial T = \Delta C_p/T$, two of the terms cancel, leaving

$$\frac{\partial \ln K}{\partial T} = \frac{\Delta H^\circ}{\partial T} \qquad (10.3)$$

the required equation.

§ 10.3 Local entropy production

In the discussion of isothermal systems we have now accepted that a reaction characterized by a loss of entropy can proceed provided that there is a greater gain of entropy by the surroundings. But this notion of compensation between entropy changes in different regions, though valid enough, has to be examined a little further if a misunderstanding is to be avoided. You are in no danger of misunderstanding if you can immediately dismiss the following riddle: How do the chemical reactants within our flask know that a great enough entropy increase will occur elsewhere to compensate for the entropy decrease associated with the reaction which is going on? In other words: Is not the principle of the universal increase of entropy rather unsatisfactory if it requires collusion between regions some distance apart?

The difficulty disappears, however, if one pays closer attention to what happens in the flask as the reaction begins. The molecules interchange energy and groups of atoms (chemical reaction) continuously, with an overall trend in the direction which maximizes the probability, and hence the entropy, locally. If a higher entropy can be achieved by increasing the kinetic energy (temperature) at the expense of some entropy associated with atomic or molecular arrangements this will occur. Locally, the group of molecules is at first effectively an isolated system, the first step in the reaction direction being taken before the heat can get away to the surroundings. As soon as the temperature begins to rise, however, a further entropy increase can be achieved by a flow of heat to adjacent cooler parts, and this goes on, with more or less efficiency according to the experimental stirring arrangements, throughout all regions until the heat developed internally to compensate the entropy loss there ultimately finds its way to the thermostat. In each element of volume in the flask therefore, what actually happens is still determined by the condition that the entropy must increase, provided only that the volume element does not contain so few molecules that fluctuations at the molecular level become important. This aspect of the second law has been emphasized by Prigogine. (See *Introduction to Thermodynamics of Irreversible Processes*, I. Prigogine, Thomas, Springfield, Illinois, 1955, Chapter 3.)

§ 10.4 The rates at which changes take place

So far, attention has been fixed upon the relationships between quantities at equilibrium and the existence of tendencies to change. In these terms it is understandable, for example, that a careful analysis of the effects of chemical substitutions on the energy and entropy of the molecules of an acid and its conjugate base can lead to predictions about the accompanying effects upon the acid dissociation constant. But nothing has been mentioned which would enable one to say which of two thermodynamically possible reactions would proceed the more rapidly, or indeed if either of them would proceed at a measurable rate at all. Certain chemical substances (hydrogen and oxygen, for instance) can exist together indefinitely without any noticeable reaction taking place, in spite of a ΔG favourable to reaction. One of the most striking examples of this kind is provided by dilute nitric acid, which is stable with respect to water and the nitrogen and oxygen in the air. As Lewis and Randall observed, 'it is to be hoped that nature will not discover a catalyst for this reaction, which would permit all of the oxygen and part of the nitrogen of the air to turn the oceans into dilute nitric acid' (*Thermodynamics*, 1st ed., McGraw-Hill, 1923, p. 568).

There are, however, two ways in which the ideas of thermodynamics have been extended into the field of rate processes. One of these, which has come to be known as 'non-equilibrium thermodynamics', focuses attention upon the rate of creation of entropy and has been found particularly valuable in describing the relationships involved when processes like diffusion and the flow of heat occur together. The rates of purely chemical changes can also be expressed simply in terms of the rate of creation of entropy, according to the methods of de Donder. (See Denbigh, *The Thermodynamics of the Steady State*, Methuen, 1951, pp. 44–49, and Prigogine and Defay, *Chemical Thermodynamics*, transl. Everett, Longmans, 1954, pp. 9–15.)

The second way of discussing reaction rates in thermodynamic terms is much more widespread and has become part of the ordinary language of reaction kinetics. During a chemical change the interacting molecules form a kind of unstable 'critical complex', regarded as being at the top of an energy barrier which must be surmounted before the products can be formed. Reaction mechanisms often involve more than one stage, and the important complex which determines the rate of the reaction is then that corresponding to the highest barrier; at this point the molecules are said to be in the 'transition state', represented by the symbol $\ddagger$. The theory is then based on two ideas:

(i) The reaction rate is directly proportional to $C_{\ddagger}$, the concentration of molecules in the transition state.

$$\text{Reaction rate} = kC_{\ddagger} \qquad (10.4)$$

(ii) The reactants and the molecules in the transition state can be treated as if in equilibrium with one another. A reaction between A and B, can thus be represented as an equilibrium between A, B and ‡, followed by the break-up of ‡:

$$A + B = \ddagger \longrightarrow \text{products} \qquad (10.5)$$

The $C_{\ddagger}$ required for (10.4) is then expressible in terms of C_A and C_B and the appropriate activity coefficients (f) as

$$C_{\ddagger} = KC_A C_B (f_A f_B / f_{\ddagger}) \qquad (10.6)$$

It is because of this assumed equilibrium that thermodynamic language comes into reaction kinetics. The complexes in the transition state are pictured as having characteristic average thermodynamic properties, just like other molecules, and this means that there is a definite free-energy increase on forming these complexes from the reactant molecules, and a corresponding equilibrium constant, $\exp [-\Delta G^{\ddagger}/RT]$. $\Delta G^{\ddagger}$ is the 'free energy of activation' and is related to the enthalpy $\Delta H^{\ddagger}$ and the entropy $\Delta S^{\ddagger}$ of activation in the usual way: $\Delta G^{\ddagger} = \Delta H^{\ddagger} - T\Delta S^{\ddagger}$.

According to the absolute reaction rate theory, the constant k in (10.4) is essentially the same for all reactions. Hence, if there were as much information available on the thermodynamic properties of transition states as of ordinary molecules the rates of chemical reactions would be just as amenable to calculation as the positions of chemical equilibria. But this state of affairs is a long way off and perhaps unattainable, since reliable methods would be required for estimating the free energies of complicated transition states independently of the kinetic experiments themselves. Nevertheless, a great deal of attention has recently been focused upon the properties of transition states, and some progress has been made in investigations of a comparative kind.

Even without the assumption of a universal specific rate constant for the reaction of the transition state, (10.4), certain reactions are sufficiently alike for the effects of changing substituents in a benzene ring, for example, to be quite regular and describable in terms of characteristic increments in $\Delta G^{\ddagger}$. Effects of this kind give rise to the important 'linear free energy relationships' of physical organic chemistry.

The consequences to the rate of a given reaction of making slight changes in the solvent medium can also sometimes be described quantitatively in terms of understandable effects upon the activity coefficients in (10.6), which in turn modify the important concentration $C_{\ddagger}$. The reactions between ions are particularly interesting in this respect because in dilute solutions, where good quantitative estimates of activity co-efficients can be made, even the transition state comes within the scope of the standard electrostatic theory. As the formulae of Chapter 7 show, the activity coefficients of ionic species in dilute aqueous solution are determined principally by their charges and the ionic strength. When two species have the same charge their activity coefficients are about the same at the same ionic strength, while the activity coefficient of a highly charged species is much lower than that of a species with a small charge. In any equilibrium involving ions of different charge types, therefore, a more highly charged species tends to be favoured by an increase in the ionic strength because its concentration has to increase to compensate for its lowered activity coefficient relative to the other species present. Exactly the same will apply to the equilibrium between the reactants and the transition state in a reaction involving ions, where the qualitative effects expected can be considered in a precise way because the charge on the transition state is simply the algebraic sum of the charges on the reactant ions.

It follows that an increase in ionic strength will accelerate a reaction between ions of the same sign (because of the increase in the concentration of the highly charged transition complex), slow down a reaction between ions of opposite sign and hardly affect a reaction between an ion and a neutral molecule in dilute aqueous solution, because of the cancellation of f_A and $f_{\ddagger}$ in (10.6), leaving only the activity coefficient of an uncharged species, which is nearly unity in dilute solution. Quantitative estimates of these effects can be made with formulae like (7.41) for the activity coefficients.

§ 10.5 Potential energy

When a diatomic molecule vibrates, the internuclear distance increases and decreases periodically, giving rise to a fluctuation in the potential energy and a compensating variation in the velocity of one nucleus relative to the other. A similar description applies when two molecules collide and are transformed during a chemical reaction, although the interatomic vibrations and potential energies then depend in rather a complicated way on all the distances between the various pairs of nuclei. For certain simplified cases it is, however, practicable to construct a 'potential energy surface', which helps in the discussion of possible reaction paths.

In such kinetic arguments the distinction is sometimes drawn between 'potential energy' and 'free energy', and this may be puzzling after reading Chapter 1, in which free energy was presented as a natural extension of the idea of potential energy. There is, however, no real conflict once it is recognized that the potential energy surfaces of reaction kinetics refer to potential energy at the local molecular level and leave out of account translations and rotations relative to other molecules. Motions of the latter kind are bound up with the temperature, and so figure in the more comprehensive thermodynamic potentials.

Even the potentials of elementary physics have more of a thermodynamic character than might at first be supposed. For example, the work of charging a parallel-plate condenser depends inversely upon the permittivity, ϵ, of the dielectric between the plates. The simple integration, using a constant value of ϵ, then implies that the temperature is also held constant, since ϵ generally decreases as the temperature is increased. It follows that heat must be evolved to keep the temperature constant during the charging process: for $d(1/\epsilon)/dT$, and therefore $d\Delta G/dT$, is positive, whence the entropy of charging must be negative (because $d\Delta G/dT = -\Delta S$). This decrease in entropy is consistent with the greater order imposed on the molecules of the dielectric by orientation in the field.

Observe that in elementary electrostatics the simple quantity calculated is ΔG and not the total energy change in the charging process. To obtain the latter, the heat evolved $(-T\Delta S)$ has to be taken into account along with the work done on the system, ΔG: $\Delta H = \Delta G + T\Delta S$. ($\Delta U$ and ΔH are taken to be the same because the density of the dielectric would not alter significantly on charging.)

Further work

Read pp. 26–35 in *Acid–Base Catalysis*, by R. P. Bell, Oxford, 1941, and pp. 296–299 and 368–369 in *Physical Chemistry*, by W. J. Moore, Longmans, 4th ed., 1963.

Read pp. 26–28 in *Boltzmann's Distribution Law*, by E. A. Guggenheim, North-Holland, 1963.

A useful, though fairly advanced, discussion of some physico-chemical problems in terms of non-equilibrium thermodynamics will be found in *Non-equilibrium Thermodynamics in Biophysics*, by A. Katchalsky and P. F. Curran, Harvard, 1965.

Problems for Chapter 10

1. As a check on the Lewis and Randall statement quoted in § 10.4, estimate the concentration of nitric acid in equilibrium at 25° with water and partial pressures of nitrogen and oxygen fixed at 0·8 and 0·2 atm respectively.

(Begin by calculating the standard free energy of the reaction

$$N_2 \text{ (g)} + \tfrac{5}{2}O_2 \text{ (g)} + H_2O \text{ (l)} = 2H^+ \text{ (aq)} + 2NO_3^- \text{ (aq)}$$

with the help of free energy tables.)

2. Use equations (10.4), (10.6) and (7.40) to derive an expression for the ionic strength dependence of the logarithm of the specific rate constant for a reaction between two ions of charges z_A and z_B in very dilute aqueous solution.

Check your answer by referring to a book on reaction kinetics.

Answers to Problems

Chapter 1

2. (a) $\frac{1}{2}$Zn (s) + TlNO$_3$ (aq, m_2) = $\frac{1}{2}$Zn (NO$_3$)$_2$ (aq, m_1) + Tl (s)
   or $\frac{1}{2}$Zn (s) + Tl$^+$ (aq, m_2) = $\frac{1}{2}$Zn^{2+} (aq, m_1) + Tl (s)
   (b) Tl (s) + $\frac{1}{2}$Pb(NO$_3$)$_2$ (aq, m_3) = TlNO$_3$ (aq, m_2) + $\frac{1}{2}$Pb (s)
   or   Tl (s) + $\frac{1}{2}$Pb^{2+} (aq, m_3) = Tl$^+$ (aq, m_2) + $\frac{1}{2}$Pb (s)
   ΔG values: (a) $-41\cdot2$ kjoule mole^{-1} ($-9\cdot85$ kcal mole^{-1})
   (b) $-20\cdot3$ kjoule mole^{-1} ($-4\cdot86$ kcal mole^{-1}).

   Addition of chemical reactions (a) and (b) gives half the chemical reaction quoted. Therefore,

   $$\Delta G \text{ for reaction quoted} = -(41\cdot2 + 20\cdot3) \times 2$$
   $$= -123\cdot0 \text{ kjoule mole}^{-1}$$
   $$(-29\cdot4 \text{ kcal mole}^{-1})$$

3. Since $\sum_i n_i \mathrm{d}\mu_i = V\mathrm{d}P$, (1.10) rearranges to

   $$\mathrm{d}G - V\mathrm{d}P = \mathrm{d}A + P\mathrm{d}V = \sum_i \mu_i \mathrm{d}n_i$$

   Setting $\mathrm{d}P$ and $\mathrm{d}V$ at zero in turn then gives the required results.

Chapter 2

1. All unstable at 25°C.
   (i) $\frac{1}{2}$N$_2$O (g) + $\frac{3}{4}$O$_2$ (g) = NO$_2$ (g). $\Delta G°_{298} = 12\cdot39 - \frac{1}{2}(24\cdot9) =$
   $-0\cdot06$ kcal equation^{-1} (i.e. per equation as written)
   $-(1\cdot987 \times 298\cdot1 \times 2\cdot303)10^{-3} \log_{10} K_p = 0\cdot06$
   $$K_p = 1\cdot1 \text{ atm}^{-\frac{1}{4}}$$

   (Clearing (i) of fractions would give $(1\cdot1)^4 = 1\cdot5$ atm^{-1})
   (ii) NO (g) + $\frac{1}{2}$O$_2$ (g) = NO$_2$ (g). $\Delta G°_{298} = 12\cdot39 - 20\cdot72 =$
   $-8\cdot33$ kcal equation^{-1}

$$\therefore \log_{10} K_p = 8 \cdot 33 / 1 \cdot 364 = 6 \cdot 11.$$
$$K_p = 1 \cdot 3 \times 10^6 \text{ atm}^{-\frac{1}{2}}$$

(Clearing (ii) of fractions would give $1 \cdot 7 \times 10^{12}$ atm^{-1})

$$K_p = p_{NO_2}/p_{NO} \times p_{O_2}^{\frac{1}{2}} = 1 \cdot 3 \times 10^6 \text{ atm}^{-\frac{1}{2}}$$

If p_{O_2} of the order of 1 atm, $p_{NO_2}/p_{NO} \sim 10^6$: i.e. only 1 part in 1 million remains as NO.

If p_{O_2} of the order of 0·1 atm, p_{NO_2}/p_{NO} only changes by the factor $\sqrt{0 \cdot 1} \sim 0 \cdot 3$.

$\therefore$ Conversion is complete.

2. $\quad \frac{1}{2}H_2$ (g) $\quad = \quad$ H (g) $\qquad$ Total moles

n moles of $H_2 \longrightarrow$

$\qquad (1 - \alpha)n \qquad\qquad 2\alpha n \qquad \longrightarrow \qquad (1 + \alpha)n$

Partial pressures

$$\left(\frac{1 - \alpha}{1 + \alpha}\right)P \quad \left(\frac{2\alpha}{1 + \alpha}\right)P \quad \text{where } P = \text{total pressure}$$

$K_p = p_H/p^{\frac{1}{2}}_{H_2} = 2\alpha P^{\frac{1}{2}}/(1 - \alpha^2)^{\frac{1}{2}}$
$-1 \cdot 364 \log_{10} K_p = 48 \cdot 57. \qquad\qquad \therefore K_p = 3 \cdot 2 \times 10^{-36} \text{ atm}^{\frac{1}{2}}$

Clearly very small indeed: $\therefore \alpha$ very small, and since $P = 1$ atm, $K_p = 2\alpha$,

$$\alpha = 1 \cdot 6 \times 10^{-36}$$

3. $\qquad\qquad\qquad N_2O_4$ (g) $= 2NO_2$ (g)

n moles of $N_2O_4 \longrightarrow (1 - \alpha)n \quad 2\alpha n \longrightarrow (1 + \alpha)n$

Partial pressures same as for problem 2.

$\quad K_p$ for equation written $= 4\alpha^2 P/(1 - \alpha^2)$.

Density found/Density calc. $= n/(1 + \alpha)n = 3/4. \therefore \alpha = 1/3.$

Hence, $K_p = 0 \cdot 5 \times 25 \cdot 8/760 = 0 \cdot 017$ atm

$\Delta G°_{273} = -(1 \cdot 987 \times 273 \cdot 1 \times 2 \cdot 303) \log_{10} (0 \cdot 017)$ cal equation^{-1}
$\qquad\qquad = 2 \cdot 21$ kcal equation^{-1}

(The half equation $\frac{1}{2}N_2O_4 = NO_2$ gives $\sqrt{0 \cdot 017}$ and $1 \cdot 105$ kcal equation^{-1})

4. Because there is no change in the number of molecules, the vapour density is independent of the extent of dissociation.

5. $\Delta G°$ is twice as great for (a) as for (b). K_p for (b) is the square-root of K_p for (a).

Chapter 3

1. (a) $-13\cdot5$ kcal mole^{-1}
   (b) $+13\cdot7$ kcal mole^{-1}
   (c) (L) $13\cdot36$ kcal mole^{-1} (B and R) $13\cdot71$ kcal mole^{-1}
2. (a) $1\cdot44$ kcal mole^{-1}, $9\cdot72$ kcal mole^{-1}
   (b) (L) $10\cdot519$ kcal mole^{-1} (B and R) $10\cdot569$ kcal mole^{-1}
3. (a) ΔH for atomization of C_2H_5OH (g)

$$= (5 \times 98\cdot2) + 80\cdot5 + 79 + 109\cdot4$$
$$= 759\cdot9 \text{ kcal mole}^{-1}$$

   ΔH for atomization of C_2H_5OH (l)

$$= 759\cdot9 + 10 = 769\cdot9 \text{ kcal mole}^{-1}$$

   ΔH for dissociation to elements

$$= 769\cdot9 - (3 \times 103\cdot2) - (\tfrac{1}{2} \times 117\cdot2) - (2 \times 170\cdot4)$$
$$= 769\cdot9 - 709\cdot0$$
$$= 60\cdot9 \text{ kcal mole}^{-1}$$

   $\therefore \Delta H$ for $2C$ (s, graphite) $+ 3H_2$ (g) $+ \tfrac{1}{2}O_2$ (g) $= C_2H_5OH$ (l)
   is approximately -61 kcal mole^{-1}.

   (b) (L) $-66\cdot356$ kcal mole^{-1} (B and R) $-67\cdot14$ kcal mole^{-1}
   (c) 1 kcal only added to $98\cdot2$ kcal sufficient to remove discrepancy.
4. (a) $H = \text{constant} + aT + (b/2)T^2 - cT^{-1}$
   (b) $H = \text{constant}' + a'T + (b'/2)T^2 + (c'/3)T^3$

Chapter 4

1. $\Delta G^\circ_{298} = -0\cdot822$ kcal equation^{-1}
   $\Delta G^\circ_{1000} = -2\cdot76$ kcal equation^{-1}
2. (a) $-2\cdot53$ kcal. ($2\cdot53$ kcal *evolved* for the amount of reaction represented by the equation.) From $(\Delta H^\circ - \Delta G^\circ) = T\Delta S^\circ$.
   (b) $\Delta H^\circ_{298} = -85\cdot85 + (2 \times 30\cdot362) = -25\cdot126$ kcal equation^{-1}
   $\Delta G^\circ_{298} = -75\cdot04 + (2 \times 26\cdot224) = -22\cdot592$ kcal equation^{-1}
   $\Delta S^\circ_{298} = 32\cdot6 + (2 \times 10\cdot206) - 15\cdot51 - (2 \times 22\cdot97)$
   $\qquad\qquad = -8\cdot438$ cal deg^{-1} equation^{-1}
   (Notice that s°_{298} for the elements is not zero.)
3. $\Delta H^\ominus_{298} = -0\cdot100$ kcal mole^{-1}
   $\Delta G^\ominus_{298} = 6\cdot49$ kcal mole^{-1}
   $\Delta S^\ominus_{298} = -22\cdot1$ cal mole^{-1} deg.$^{-1}$
   $K_a = \text{antilog} (-4\cdot75) = 1\cdot78 \times 10^5$

Very large entropy decrease (due to the ordering effects on the solvent of the ions formed): important in determining position of equilibrium, since energy change practically zero.

4. $|Q_2| \ngtr Q_1$ (i.e. $|Q_2| \leqslant Q_1$), since heat would be transported to a higher temperature with no overall work done. But working the pair of cycles the other way round gives, similarly, $Q_1 \ngtr |Q_2|$ (i.e. $|Q_2| \geqslant Q_1$).

The only way of satisfying both is $|Q_2| = Q_1$. But the work terms are also equal in magnitude: $\therefore W_2/Q_2 = W_1/Q_1$.

Chapter 5

1. Take $2 \cdot 303 \times 1 \cdot 987 \times 3/2 \log_{10}$ (A.Wt.) from each number and obtain $26 \cdot 00$, $26 \cdot 00$, $26 \cdot 01$, $26 \cdot 01$, $26 \cdot 03$, $26 \cdot 03$.

2. s°_{298}: for H_2 (g) $24 \cdot 42 + 2{,}024/298 \cdot 15 = 31 \cdot 21$ e.u. ((L): $31 \cdot 211$ e.u.)

for N_2 (g) $38 \cdot 82 + 2{,}072/298 \cdot 15 = 45 \cdot 75$ e.u. ((L): $45 \cdot 767$ e.u.)

3. The required formula is

$$-\frac{\Delta G^\circ}{T} = -\frac{\Delta(G^\circ - H^\circ_0)}{T} - \frac{\Delta(\nu \Delta H^\circ_0)}{T}$$

At $1{,}000^\circ K$, $-\Delta G^\circ/T = 2(44 \cdot 23) - 64 \cdot 40 - [2(25{,}610) - 15{,}660]/1{,}000 = -11 \cdot 50$ e.u.

$\therefore \Delta G^\circ_{1000} = \underline{11 \cdot 5 \text{ kcal.}}$

$2 \cdot 303R \log_{10} K_p = -\Delta G^\circ/T$.

$\therefore K_p = \text{antilog}_{10} [-11 \cdot 5/4 \cdot 57] = \underline{3 \cdot 02 \times 10^{-3} \text{ atm.}}$

At $2{,}000^\circ K$, $-\Delta G^\circ/T = 2(47 \cdot 68) - 70 \cdot 52 - [2(25{,}610) - 15{,}660]/2{,}000 = 7 \cdot 06$ e.u.

$\therefore \Delta G^\circ_{2000} = \underline{-14 \cdot 12 \text{ kcal.}}$

$K_p = \text{antilog}_{10} \underline{[7 \cdot 06/4 \cdot 57] = 34 \cdot 9 \text{ atm.}}$

4. $\Delta s = R \ln (v_2/v_1)$

5. Benzene: $l_v/T_b = 94 \cdot 16 \times 78/(273 \cdot 15 + 80 \cdot 1) = 20 \cdot 8$ e.u.
Ether: $l_v/T_b = 89 \cdot 08 \times 74/(273 \cdot 15 + 34 \cdot 60) = 21 \cdot 5$ e.u.

Trouton's Rule says that entropies of vaporization at the boiling-point are about 21 e.u. for normal liquids.

6. Since the reaction involves the loss of 2 moles of gas, expect $\Delta S \simeq -42$ e.u.

(L) p.91 gives $(2 \times 46.01) - 45.767 - (3 \times 31.211) = -47.38$ e.u.

∴ a rough idea of the magnitude is obtained.

7. The unidirectional kinetic energy upon impact is finally randomized in the surroundings as heat, with entropy increase $-\Delta U/T$.

Chapter 6

1. At 1.5% $v_{C_2H_5OH} = 54.5$ cm^3, $v_{H_2O} = 18.03$ cm^3.
   At 99.5% $v_{C_2H_5OH} = 58.1$ cm^3, $v_{H_2O} = 13.81$ cm^3.

2. T is required for which $(\Delta G^\circ/T) = 0$ since $K_p = 1$ for $p_{N_2} = p_{O_2} = p_{NO}$.

   The easiest form to use is

$$R \ln (K_2/K_1) = -(\Delta G^\circ_T/T)_T + (\Delta G^\circ/298\cdot15)$$
$$= -\Delta H^\circ(1/T - 1/298\cdot15)$$
$$\therefore 20\cdot719 = -21\cdot600 (298\cdot15/T - 1)$$
$$T = 7,310^\circ K$$

   ∴ approximate temperature $7,000^\circ$C.

3. (a) $R \ln K = B - \dfrac{A}{T} + a \ln T + \dfrac{b}{2} T + \dfrac{c}{2} T^{-2}$

   (b) $R \ln K = B' - \dfrac{A'}{T} + a' \ln T + \dfrac{b'}{2} T + \dfrac{c'}{6} T^2$

4. The function $-(\Delta G^\circ - \Delta H^\circ_{298})/T$ for the whole reaction turns out to be $38\cdot19$ cal deg^{-1} at 500°K and $37\cdot14$ cal deg^{-1} at $1,000^\circ$K, thus illustrating the much smaller temperature variation of the difference than of the individual terms. Simple linear interpolation then gives $37\cdot51$ cal mole^{-1} for 823°K, and with $\Delta H^\circ_{298} = 42\cdot608$ kcal mole^{-1}, this leads to $\Delta G^\circ/T = -14\cdot29$ at 823°K and $\log_{10} K = \log_{10} p_{CO_2} = -3\cdot12$.

   Thus $p_{CO_2} = 760 \times 7\cdot6 \times 10^{-4} = 0\cdot58$ mm Hg

   This is about $0\cdot08\%$ of the atmospheric pressure. The volume percentage of CO_2 in air is generally about $0\cdot03$, so there is a tendency for $CaCO_3$ to decompose at this temperature.

   (L), pp. 128 and 318, yields $\Delta G^\circ_{298} = 31\cdot12$ kcal, $\Delta H^\circ_{298} =$

42·50 kcal. By (6.20), $\log_{10} K = \log_{10} p \simeq -2.95$ at 823°K. So $p_{CO_2} \simeq 0.85$ mm Hg.

This gives some idea of the degree of reliability of the simple calculation: very useful for orders of magnitude and short extrapolations, less reliable where accuracy is critical.

Chapter 7

1. An important step is $x_2 + x_1 = 1$; $\therefore$ $dx_2 = -dx_1$.

2. (a) This uses the previous answer to remove the x parts of the activities, leaving only the f parts.
   (b) Again the usual stumbling-block is $dx_2 = -dx_1$.

3. At 352°C, $2.303RT/F = 0.124$ when R in *joule* deg^{-1} mole^{-1}.
   At 478°C, $2.303RT/F = 0.149$ when R in *joule* deg^{-1} mole^{-1}.
   f_1 values at 352°C are 2·30, 1·71, 1·50 and 1·12;
   at 478°C, 1·78, 1·47, 1·32 and 1·08.
   They obey (7.23) fairly well and vary with temperature as expected (less deviation at the higher temperature).

   a_2 is obtained from x_2 and f_2, the latter requiring the use of the determined B/RT for f_1, in accordance with (7.23) and (7.24).

4. (a) $x_2p_2° = 0.2 \times 1{,}823 = \underline{365}$ mm Hg.
   (b) $B \simeq 95 (9.15 - 6.7)^2 = 569$ cal mole^{-1}
   $\therefore$ $2.303 \times 1.987 \times 298.15 \log_{10} f_2 = 569 \times (0.8)^2 = 364$.
   $\therefore$ $f_2 = 1.85$.
   $x_2p_2°f_2 = 365 \times 1.85 = \underline{676}$ mm Hg.
   $\therefore$ (b) much better than (a) and quite a good estimate.

5. (7.42) has $K = 10^{-9.24} = 5.75 \times 10^{-10}$ mole kg^{-1}
   (7.44) has $K = 10^{-4.756} = 1.754 \times 10^{-5}$ mole kg^{-1}
   (7.46) has $K = 10^{-3.77} = 1.70 \times 10^{-4}$ mole kg^{-1}

6. $$Ca^{2+} + Fe(CN)_6^{4-} = CaFe(CN)_6^{-2}$$
   $$(2-\alpha)m \quad (1-\alpha)m \quad \alpha m$$

   $$I = \frac{m}{2}[4(2-\alpha) + 16(1-\alpha) + 4\alpha] = \underline{4m(3-2\alpha)}$$
   $$= 0.04(3-2\alpha)$$

   From (7.47), when $m = 0.01$,
   $$\log_{10} \frac{(2-\alpha)(1-\alpha)}{\alpha} = -1.77 + 8\left[\frac{I^{\frac{1}{2}}}{1+I^{\frac{1}{2}}} - 0.3I\right]$$

1st approximation

$$\alpha \simeq 0.8, \quad \therefore I \simeq 0.04(1.4) = 0.056$$
$$[I^{\frac{1}{2}}/(1 + I^{\frac{1}{2}}) - 0.3I] = 0.191 - 0.017 = 0.174$$

$$\therefore \log_{10} 1.2 \left(\frac{1 - \alpha}{\alpha}\right) \simeq -1.77 + 1.39 = -0.38$$

$$\therefore \left(\frac{1 - \alpha}{\alpha}\right) \simeq \frac{0.24}{1.2} = 0.20 \qquad \alpha \simeq \frac{1}{1.20} = 0.83$$

2nd approximation

$$\alpha \simeq 0.83. \quad \therefore I \simeq 0.054$$
$$[I^{\frac{1}{2}}/(1 + I^{\frac{1}{2}}) - 0.3I] \simeq 0.188 - 0.016 = 0.172$$

$$\therefore \log_{10} 1.17 \left(\frac{1 - \alpha}{\alpha}\right) \simeq -1.77 + 1.38 = -0.39$$

$$\therefore \frac{1 - \alpha}{\alpha} \simeq \frac{0.245}{1.17} = 0.209$$

$$\underline{\alpha = 0.83}$$

Notice: (*a*) the anion is largely in the ion pair form;
(*b*) the activity coefficient term affects the calculation by introducing a factor of about 25 even at $0.01 M$ in this case.

Chapter 8

1. 0.08%. (18 cm^3 in 22.4 l.)

2. Use $\delta T = (\Delta v/\Delta s)\delta P$, where $\delta P = -1$ atm $= -1.01325 \times 10^6$ erg cm^{-3}. (See § 2.3.)

    Easier to keep Δv and Δs in quantities per g this time:
$$\Delta v = -(1.090 - 1.000) = -0.090 \text{ cm}^3 \text{ g}^{-1}$$
$$\Delta s = 80/273 \text{ cal g}^{-1} \text{ deg}^{-1}$$
$$\therefore \Delta v/\Delta s = -0.09 \times 273/80 \times 4.184 \times 10^7 \text{ cm}^3 \text{ deg erg}^{-1}$$

    Then δT becomes $+0.0074$ deg; i.e. triple point is at $\underline{+0.0074°\text{C}}$.
$k_f = 1.987 \times (273.15)^2/1,000 \times 80 = 1.85$ deg mole^{-1} kg.
($m_1 l_f = $ no. of moles in 1 kg $\times$ latent heat per mole $= $ no. of g in 1 kg $\times$ latent heat per g.)

3. (*a*) All except ice I have positive dT/dP and therefore positive Δv; i.e. all but ice I would sink in water.

    (*b*) If no point is deeper than 9 km the pressure never exceeds 1,000 atm, which is under half that required to form ice III at $-20°C$. Thus the pressure is never great enough to produce the forms stable at higher temperatures. (The salinity would also depress the temperatures somewhat.)

4. An equation like (8.8) but with $^g\mu_B$ for $^s\mu_B$ on the right-hand side can be set up immediately, since the elevation of b.pt. implies a constant vapour pressure (1 atm) for comparison.

The principal differences from the freezing-point case are that (8.9) (with $^gh_B - {}^lh_B$ for $^lh_B - {}^sh_B$) has a negative sign because the solution phase is now the phase of lower entropy, but this sign change goes out when θ is put as $T - T_b$ in this case, so that $d\theta$ and dT have the same sign.

The final formula is therefore just like (8.12) but with T_b for T_f and l_v for l_f.

5. (a) For pure $Ca(IO_3)_2$ solutions, $I = \frac{1}{2}(4m_{Ca^{++}} + m_{IO_3^-}) = 3m_2$, since $m_{IO_3^-} = 2m_2 = 2m_{Ca^{++}}$.

Ignore the difference between molality and molarity: $I = 0.02352$ and $I^{\frac{1}{2}}/(1 + I^{\frac{1}{2}}) - 0.3I = 0.126$.

In absence of common ions,

$$\begin{aligned}
\log_{10} K_s &= \log_{10} [m_2 \times (2m_2)^2] + 3 \log_{10} \gamma_\pm \\
&= \log_{10} 4 + 3 \log_{10} m_2 + 3 \log_{10} \gamma_\pm \\
&= \overline{7}.907
\end{aligned}$$

$$\therefore K_s = \underline{8.1 \times 10^{-7}}$$

(Note that here

$$\begin{aligned}
3 \log_{10} \gamma_\pm &= \log_{10} \gamma_{Ca^{++}} + 2 \log_{10} \gamma_{IO_3^-} \\
&= -0.5 [4 + 2] [I^{\frac{1}{2}}/(1 + I^{\frac{1}{2}}) - 0.3I])
\end{aligned}$$

(b) Say I changes from 0.0235 to about 0.13 (allowing for some increase in solubility). Now $I^{\frac{1}{2}}/(1 + I^{\frac{1}{2}}) - 0.3I \simeq 0.226$. In the above formula for $\log_{10} K_s$ the variables occur in the combination $3 \log_{10} m_2 + 3 \log_{10} \gamma_\pm$. Thus any decrease in $\log_{10} \gamma_\pm$ shows up directly as an increase in $\log_{10} m_2$. The change in $\log_{10} \gamma_\pm$ caused by the addition of the NaCl is simply

$$-(0.5 \times 2)(0.226 - 0.126) = -0.10$$

But 0.10 is $\log_{10} 1.26$, whence $\gamma_\pm$ decreases by about 26% and m_2, the solubility of the iodate, increases by *about* 26%.

6. (a) The diagram must have steps: the equilibrium vapour pressure is fixed at a constant temperature when 3 phases are present (vapour and 2 solids; or vapour, saturated solution

and 1 solid). See, e.g., Moore, 4th ed., p. 145. Note that a single hydrate has no fixed vapour pressure, only a range within which it is stable, and discuss deliquescence and efflorescence.

(b) ϕ values give the water activities (by (7.21)) and hence the vapour pressures of the unsaturated solutions. The diagram can therefore be extended from the saturated solution to the pure water axis. (For a ϕ table see Robinson and Stokes, *Electrolyte Solutions*, 1955, p. 474; table 7 of appendix 8.10.)

(c) The results are incompatible. The Foote and Scholes method would be least reliable when the equilibrating solution approaches 100% alcohol. Extrapolation of more conventional vapour-pressure determinations at higher temperatures is probably more reliable for very low pressures like this.

Chapter 9

1. (L), p. 39, gives OH^- (aq) as $-37,595$ cal, H_2O (l) as $-56,690$ cal.

$$H_2O \text{ (l)} = H^+ \text{ (aq)} + OH^- \text{ (aq)}$$
$$\Delta G^\ominus = -RT \ln K_w = \mu^\ominus_{H^+} + \mu^\ominus_{OH^-} - \mu^\circ_{H_2O} = 19,095$$
$$\therefore \log_{10} K_w = -19,095/1,364 = -13.99.$$
$$K_w = 1.02 \times 10^{-14} \text{ mole}^2 \text{ (kg solvent)}^{-2}$$

2. Use the $e^\ominus$ values from Table 9.1. Note that for a rough calculation dilution effects do not matter, as only *ratios* of concentrations are required.

   A sharp change is found at the end-point.

3. $p_{H_2} = P_{\text{atmos.}} - p_{H_2O} = (750 - 20)/760 = 0.960$ atm.

$$e_H = e^\ominus_H + 0.059 \log_{10} (H^+)/p^{\frac{1}{2}}_{H_2}$$
$$\therefore e_H + 0.0295 \log_{10} p_{H_2} = e^\ominus_H + 0.059 \log_{10} (H^+)$$

The quantity $0.0295 \log_{10} 0.960$ has therefore to be added to e_H: i.e. 0.53 mV has to be *subtracted*.

4. (a) Hg_2^{2+}: the ion has to be doubly charged.

   (b) $0.268 = 0.789 + 0.0295 \log_{10} (Hg_2^{2+})$ when $a_{Cl^-} = 1$.
   i.e. $0.268 = 0.789 + 0.0295 \log_{10} K_s$

$$K_s = \text{antilog}_{10} (-0.521/0.0295) = \text{antilog}_{10} (-17.63)$$
$$= 2.4 \times 10^{-18} \text{ mole}^2 \text{ (kg solvent)}^{-2}$$

(for Hg_2Cl_2 (s) $= Hg_2^{2+}$ (aq) $+ 2Cl^-$ (aq)).

5. (a) $IO_3^- + 6H^+ + 5e^- = \frac{1}{2}I_2 + 3H_2O$ $e^\ominus = +1\cdot195$ v.

  (b) $IO_3^- + 6H^+ + Cl^- + 4e^- = ICl + 3H_2O$ $e^\ominus = +0\cdot648$ v.

    $(\Delta G^\ominus = -4\cdot0 - (3 \times 56\cdot59) + 32\cdot25 + 31\cdot35$ kcal from tables 16, 11, 14, $= -110\cdot47$ kcal $= -250$ kjoule $= -4F e^\ominus$.)

  (c) $H_3AsO_4 + 2H^+ + 2e^- = HAsO_2 + 2H_2O$ $e^\ominus = +0\cdot559$ v.

  (d) $MnO_4^- + 2H_2O + 3e^- = MnO_2 + 4OH^-$

$$e^\ominus = +0\cdot588 \text{ v.}$$

(p. 238; or begin with

$$MnO_4^- + 4H^+ + 3e^- = MnO_2 + 2H_2O \qquad e^\ominus = +1\cdot695 \text{ v.}$$
$$\Delta G^\ominus = -3F\,(1\cdot695) \text{ joule.}$$

Add $4H_2O = 4H^+ + 4OH^-$

$$\Delta G^\ominus = -4RT \ln K_w$$
$$= +4 \times 1,364 \times 13\cdot99 = 76,300 \text{ cal}$$

$\therefore$ required reaction has

$$\Delta G^\ominus = (76,300 \times 4\cdot184) - 3F\,(1\cdot695) \text{ joule}$$
$$\therefore e^\ominus = -(76,300 \times 4\cdot184/3F) + 1\cdot695 \text{ volt})$$

Chapter 10

1. $\Delta G^\ominus_{298} = (2 \times -26\cdot43) - (-56\cdot69) = +3\cdot83$ kcal equation^{-1}.

$\therefore \log_{10} K = -3\cdot81/1\cdot364 = \bar{3}\cdot19.$

$\therefore K = 1\cdot55 \times 10^{-3} = (H^+)^2\,(NO_3^-)^2/p_{N_2}p_{O_2}^{5/2}$
$\quad = m^4\gamma_\pm^4/0\cdot8 \times (0\cdot2)^{5/2}$

$\therefore m\gamma_\pm = 0\cdot069$

By (7.41) $\gamma_\pm$ is estimated to have a value of 0·8 at molalities between 0·08 and 0·1. Hence $m = 0\cdot069/0\cdot8 = 0\cdot086$.

The molality of nitric acid at equilibrium is therefore about 0·09.

Summary of Principal Equations

(a) The two most important equations are
$$\Delta G^{\ominus} = -RT \ln K \qquad (2.17)$$
by which equilibrium constants can be calculated from free energy tables, and
$$\left(\frac{\partial \ln K}{\partial T} \right)_P = \frac{\Delta H^{\ominus}}{RT^2} \qquad (6.19)$$
which gives the variation of equilibrium constants with temperature. When $-(g^{\circ} - h^{\circ})/T$ tables are available the second equation can be by-passed.

At a fixed temperature,
$$\Delta G^{\ominus} = \Delta H^{\ominus} - T\Delta S^{\ominus} \qquad (4.16)$$

(b) Effects of changes of conditions on chemical potentials are calculated from:

$\partial \mu_i / \partial T = -s_i$ (6.27), $\partial(\mu_i/T)/\partial T = -h_i/T^2$ (6.29), $\partial \mu_i / \partial P = v_i$ (6.28)

$\partial \mu_i / \partial \ln a_i = RT$ from (2.15), $\partial(\mu_i/T)/\partial \ln a_i = R$ from (2.15).

Note also: $\mu_i = \mu^{\circ}_i + RT \ln p_i$ for a gas phase component,
$$\mu_i = \mu^{\ominus}_i + RT \ln a_i \text{ in general.}$$

(c) The starting-point of the Gibbs derivations (§ 6.3) is
$$dU = TdS - PdV + \sum_i \mu_i dn_i \qquad (6.2)$$

(d) Useful entropy equations:

$S = k \ln \mathscr{P}$ (4.11), $\qquad\qquad dS = dQ/T$ (4.13),

and $s_{T'} = \int_0^{T'} c \ln T + \Sigma l/T$ for all phase changes (§ 5.6).

(e) The phase rule, $\qquad\qquad F = C + 2 - P \qquad (8.1)$

$$\ln \left(\frac{p_i}{p_i^{\circ}} \right) = -\frac{l_v}{R} \left(\frac{1}{T} - \frac{1}{T^{\circ}} \right) \qquad (8.6)$$

for the variation of vapour pressure with temperature (l_v assumed constant and replaced by l_s for sublimation).

$$\ln x_i = -\frac{l_f}{R}\left(\frac{1}{T} - \frac{1}{T_f}\right) \qquad (8.11)$$

the perfect solubility equation (l_f assumed constant and the solution assumed perfect), from which the formula for the cryoscopic constant $RT^2/m_1 l_f$ can be obtained.

(f) Equations involving electromotive force:

$$\Delta G = -nFE \qquad (1.9)$$
$$\Delta H = -nFE + nFT\,(\partial E/\partial T) \qquad (6.24)$$

$$E = E^\ominus + \frac{RT}{nF}\ln\frac{(A)^{\nu_A}(B)^{\nu_B}\ldots}{(C)^{\nu_C}(D)^{\nu_D}\ldots} \qquad (9.12)$$

A special case of the latter is

$$e = e^\ominus + \frac{0.059}{z_i}\log_{10} a_i \qquad (\S\ 9.5 \text{ and } 9.7)$$

for the potential at $25°C$ of an electrode reversible to an ion of charge z_i units (e.g. $z_i = +2$ for Cu^{2+} and -1 for Cl^-).

Index